THE COMPLETE COLOUR, STYLE AND IMAGE BOOK

ACKNOWLEDGEMENTS

Many different individuals and companies helped with the preparation of this book. My thanks to the following people:

Michele Turney at Thorsons (HarperCollins) for looking at the manuscript objectively and making it into a better book.

My husband, Brian, who helped with typing and gave me much encouragement and love when it was needed most.

My agent, Susan Mears, for her encouragement and faith in my abilities to write this book.

Denise Dane for her efforts in the first edit of the book.

Vicki Braithwait of Direct Colour Promotions, Sheffield, who supplied the precision-dyed fabrics which were used in the colour exercises and wheels in chapters 1 and 2.

O.J. Stewart-Liberty, on behalf of Liberty of London Prints Ltd., for his kind permission to include the Liberty fabric prints in chapter 2.

Marie Williams of La Creme, Sheffield, who supplied direction and hair samples for chapter 2.

Woman's Weekly magazine and beauty editor Clare Grundy for giving their time and kind permission to use some of the photographs of the models in chapter 2.

The marketing department at Bristol Myers (Clairol) for their permission to use some of the photographs of the models in chapter 2.

My friend, Marianne Brown, who agreed to model at very short notice for some of the pictures in chapter 2.

The Image Bank for the photograph on page 14.

Tie Rack Ltd., for permission to use the illustrations and suggestions given in the section on scarves in chapter 5.

John Doughty of Nature's Sunshine Products Inc., for permission to reproduce their Body Type Characteristics questionnaire and chart in chapter 7.

THE COMPLETE COLOUR, STYLE AND IMAGE BOOK

A comprehensive guide to looking your best

BARBARA JACQUES

Thorsons
An Imprint of HarperCollins*Publishers*

An Imprint of HarperCollins*Publishers*
77–85 Fulham Palace Road,
Hammersmith, London W6 8JB
1160 Battery Street,
San Francisco, California 94111–1213

Published by Thorsons 1994
1 3 5 7 9 10 8 6 4 2

A catalogue record for this book is available from the
British Library

ISBN 0 7225 2977 5

Printed in Italy by Rotolito Lombarda

CONTENTS

INTRODUCTION

When you look in the mirror, you see a highly individual combination of colours. The colour of your hair and skin may be similar to that of many other people, but in subtle ways your colouring is as unique as your personality.

Colour is a major factor in your personal image. Every morning when you get dressed you make colour choices – deciding which outfit to wear and the accessories to complement it. But are you making the right decisions? Despite the importance of colour to the way in which we present ourselves to the world, how many of us really understand it?

We are rarely left to reach our own decisions about colour. During our formative years, mothers and teachers may recommend colours for us based on their preferences, without considering our personal colouring. And if they express disapproval of any colours we choose ourselves, this can restrict our choices throughout our lives and take away any colour confidence and creativity we might have had. Even colour consultants, to whom we often turn as adults, can be misguided in their advice.

It may surprise you to learn that we can all wear *every* colour to look and feel great. The secret is to find out how 'you' can personally wear each colour best, enabling you to be as creative as you want. This book reveals how you can make colour and style work for you. It shows you how to dress with confidence, secure in the knowledge that you are making the most of yourself with your unique skin and hair colouring and body shape. All you need to do is learn the few simple rules of colour and style that are explained in this book.

Every year I speak to thousands of people, many of whom devote their entire working lives to advising on colour or working with it. Relatively few of them, however, understand the fascinating rules of colour. Even students of art or design are generally poorly informed about colour, proportion and line. When you understand colour in relation to your own 'colour personality', you will be able to be far more confident about yourself and the image you present. Understanding how your body absorbs, transmits and reflects light energy will enable you to use colour more effectively and gain access to the light within you.

Try to read this book with an open mind and dismiss any preconditioning you may have had regarding your best colours. Understanding how colour really works will help build your confidence and bring a spark to your individual creativity and style.

Chapter 1

THE MAGIC OF COLOUR

Colour is magic, as anyone with insight into it will tell you. A true understanding of colour is the first step towards looking and feeling good by dressing with style. Later chapters show you how to use colour with confidence in clothes, make-up and in your surroundings, but first it is essential to get to grips with the basics, and to find out how we perceive colour through our powerful sense of sight.

Colour and Sight

Many of us take colour for granted, not realizing the complexity of the process that enables us to perceive it. Our eyes are highly sophisticated organs that transmit detailed information to the brain. Light –

the stimulus that provides this information – is transferred through approximately 120 million rods and 6 million cones in the eye. The rods are responsible for night vision and the cones are responsible for day vision.

The light wavelengths that are trans-

When you look at yourself in the mirror, the transmitted and reflected light wavelengths are colour-coded by the brain. The illustration shows examples of colours and their wavelengths.

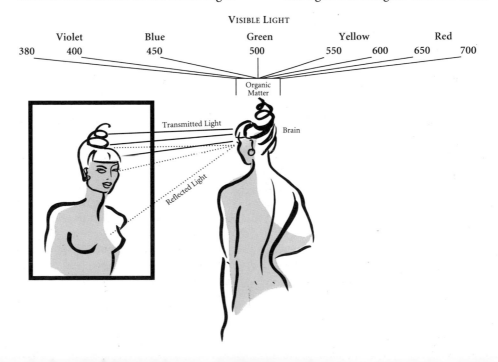

VISIBLE LIGHT

Violet	Blue	Green	Yellow	Red
380 400	450	500	550 600	650 700

Organic Matter

Transmitted Light

Brain

Reflected Light

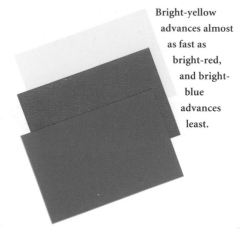

Bright-yellow advances almost as fast as bright-red, and bright-blue advances least.

The darker colour (yellow with red) advances and the lighter colour (yellow with green) recedes. The lighter-coloured square occupies more space visually, so it appears larger.

The warm colour (red with yellow) advances faster than the cooler colour (red with blue).

ferred to the brain possess no colour in themselves. The brain colour-codes these wavelengths according to the speed at which they travel, and from the amount of absorbed or transmitted light that accompanies them. In other words, our surroundings and objects around us do not possess innate colour, but rather our brain codes the different light wavelengths emanating from them. And subtle differences in our genetic make-up can affect our perception of colour, as in colour blindness, for example.

How Colour Travels

Light travels at different speeds. As a general rule, dark colours travel faster than light colours; bright colours travel faster than muted colours; and warm colours travel faster than cool colours. The colours that travel fast are termed 'advancing' colours; those that travel slowly are 'receding'.

The warm blue (blue with red) advances faster than the cool blue (blue with yellow).

Advancing colours always appear more dominant than receding colours. Being aware of these properties is an important part of making colours work for you. You will generally need to allocate less space to a dominant, advancing colour, and to create a harmonious balance between advancing and less advancing colours. If you allow one colour to dominate, it will influence the mood created. A cool background colour will make warm colours advance more than they will on a warm background, and vice versa.

As you study the examples (on this page), you will start to become increasingly aware of the different effects of colour combinations in terms of their characteristics of intensity (light and dark shades), clarity (bright and muted shades) and undertone (warm and cool shades). A greater understanding of colour co-ordination and management will help you select the colours to wear and the environment you wish to create.

You can change the appearance of a colour by placing it alongside another colour. Orange–red either side of primary red, for example, makes the primary red look cooler (see top illustration). Blue–red either side of primary red makes the primary red look warmer (see bottom illustration).

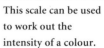

This scale can be used to work out the intensity of a colour.

Six greens, all with different characteristics.

Recognizing Colour Characteristics

Most people have little knowledge of how colour actually works. Try the following exercise to test your colour awareness. Look at the six greens illustrated (left). Try to work out which green is light, which one is dark, and which are muted, bright, warm and cool. You will probably find it easiest to spot the light and dark pair (first and second from top respectively). Finding the muted and bright pair is a little more difficult (third and fourth); and many people do not even realize that the fifth and sixth are warm and cool respectively.

Intensity
The intensity of a colour – how light or dark it is – can be determined by relating it to the black–grey–white scale shown (above) (colour combinations can also be analysed in this way). While all three dimensions of colour (intensity, clarity, undertone) have a definite role to play in personal colour analysis, intensity is, in my view, the most important dimension. It is known to have a direct effect on the unconscious brain, and is the first dimension to be recognized by the uninitiated in colour. For the wearer, artist and dress designer, it provides a rule of thumb and

a starting point from which to work. By working out the intensity of a colour, you can then decide which other colours will work well with it to create the desired effect.

Clarity
Clarity is a measure of how clear or muted a colour is. The more colours that are mixed to produce a particular colour, the more toned-down or muted it becomes. Mixing is used as a yardstick to determine whether a colour belongs to a bright category or a muted one.

Undertone
Red and yellow colour hues are considered warm, whereas blues and greens are considered cool. This, however, is a very generalized 'temperature' classification. Some reds, for example, could be considered comparatively cool when contrasted with another red with a visible yellow content. Warm colours appear warmer and cool colours cooler when contrasted with their opposites in temperature (see page 2). This reinforces the belief that colours are affected by what is placed alongside them. When it comes to the undertone in people's colouring, all warm-blooded creatures have some degree of warmth in them and a lesser degree of coolness which appears to increase with age.

The Colour Wheel

The wheel was devised by Sir Isaac Newton (1642–1727) who used it to analyse the composition of the light spectrum. Over the years, the wheel has been adapted in many ways, but the basic principle has remained the same – the colours of the rainbow in the sequence in which the brain perceives them.

The wheel on the facing page shows the primary colours (yellow, blue and red), the secondary or complementary colours (green, violet and orange) and the intermediate colours (yellow–green, blue–green, blue–violet, red–violet, red–orange and yellow–orange).

Developing Colour Logic

During my many years of working with colour, I have frequently turned to the colour wheel as a useful tool for explaining, organizing and studying colour relationships. Look at the three primary colours on the wheel – red, yellow and blue. They generate a certain 'feeling' or 'undertone' which can be defined as 'warm' or 'cool'. Red projects a feeling of warmth as we associate it with fire. Similarly, yellow projects a feeling of warmth as we associate it with sunshine. In contrast, blue projects a cool feeling, like water.

When, however, you look at the secondary colours of green and violet, you will find that they generate a mixture of both warm and cool feelings. When you try to visualize these colours you may experience some difficulty in classifying them; this is because one warm-feeling and one cool-feeling colour effectively cancel each other out. The third secondary colour is quite different. When you mix the warm colours of red and yellow together, the effect is to strengthen the warm feeling and to generate a warm undertone. This is why orange can never be made to look cool.

Colour Relationships and Terms

The colour wheel can be used in a variety of easy sequences to show how one colour relates to another. To discover if colours are related or not is simply a matter of finding out if they have a common denominator. For example, blue–violet is a distant relative of blue–green, blue being the common denominator.

Colours termed 'complementary' are best described as those directly opposite one another on the colour wheel. For example, red is the complementary colour to green. Split complementary colours are found on either side of the opposite complementary colour. On either side of red, for example, appears red–violet and red–orange; these are the split complementaries of green.

The vocabulary of colour is not universally recognized, hence a colour used for a wedding in one country may well be used for a funeral in another. I believe the most practical way to describe a colour is to use its characteristics of intensity, clarity and undertone.

By adding a colour characteristic to the name most commonly used for the colour or colour combination, it becomes more meaningful to the wearer than telling him or her simply to wear red, for example. This eliminates the question most frequently

asked by the wearer – which particular red is appropriate?

Finding the perfect intensity of a particular colour for you is virtually impossible. It is much better to be aware of each area of colour intensity that will look good on you. This will give you more choice and a better chance of finding what you are looking for when it comes to replenishing your wardrobe, or planning colours with which to surround yourself.

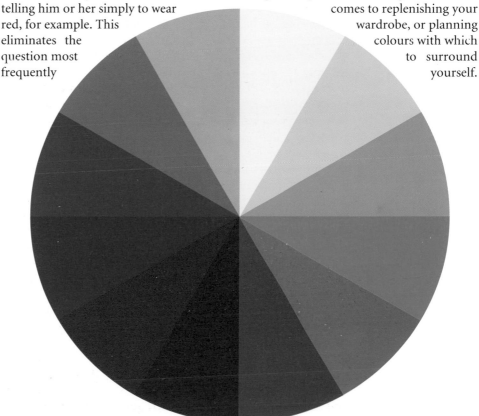

The Colour Wheel

Colour Harmonies

In any colour arrangement, careful selection is crucial. To help you make informed choices, here are some basic facts about how colours harmonize.

Monochrome Harmonies

If you observe a tree or bush closely you will see that the leaves are coloured several shades of green. Such a colour harmony consisting of several shades of one colour is called 'monochrome', or 'mono' for short. If you choose to wear a mono look, it is important that the end result complements your own level of contrast. For example, if your natural colouring is light, the light to medium shade of the mono colour will be more flattering near the face, graduating downwards to a darker shade of the same colour, and vice versa.

Analogous Harmonies

Also known as 'blood relative' colour harmonies, analogous harmonies consist of colours found side by side on the colour wheel. These harmonies are more 'active' than the mono look.

Contrast Harmonies

These are the most visually exciting of all colour harmonies. Used carefully, they can bring your look vividly to life. Contrast harmonies can, for example, consist of a complementary colour contrasted with its opposing primary colour. To create a balanced, harmonious look you will need to use a complementary colour from a different intensity, or give the less dominant, complementary colour more space. For example, blue and its complementary colour orange taken from the same intensity colour wheel would visibly be very active, and in some cases jar on the nerves. By changing one of the colours, say the blue for navy, and using this as the predominant colour, then adding a small amount of orange could be very attractive, easier on the eye and creative for the wearer. Alternatively, as illustrated (left), you could use an arbitrator or neutral colour to lift and separate your two complementary colours.

Colour Imaging

First-hand experience of how our visual system works with regard to colour comes from practising simple 'colour imaging'. This technique has fascinated many of my students, and encouraged them to develop an inquiring attitude towards colour theory and their personal colouring.

Colour-imaging enables us to understand how scientists derived the colour wheel. Look at the following illustration. If you concentrate your gaze on the primary-red square for 30–40 seconds and then focus on the empty square on

Neutral colours can be used between complementary colours to good effect.

Concentrating on the squares on the left, then looking at the empty squares on the right, produces an 'after image'.

ous contrast', the effect resulting from placing two different colours side by side.

After images are usually much lighter in intensity. First, this is because our visual system reduces the transmission of the dominant colour reaching the eye's retina, thus creating the after image. Second, the eye's retina transmits the white light surrounding the dominant colour. If, however, you view a dominant colour on a black background, the after image is much darker in intensity. As anticipated, the eye's retina simply absorbs the black light surrounding the dominant colour.

You should now be able to discover any colour's complementary colour. This is a great advantage when it comes to selecting colours for your wardrobe.

the right, you will see what is called an 'after image'. For each of the primary colours – red, yellow and blue – you will find that the after images seen are their opposite, complementary colours.

To understand the selective nature of your visual system you need to view a primary colour and its complementary colour together. The following exercise enables you to appreciate your brain's adaptive capabilities. Look at the illustration (right). Starting at the top, focus on the yellow and violet box for 30–40 seconds, then transfer your gaze to the empty box on the right. You will see that the colours 'swop' over – the violet will be on the outside and the yellow on the inside. This phenomenon is known as 'simultane-

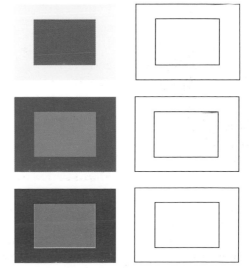

RIGHT: When you look at complementary colours together, the after image will show them turned inside out.

Chapter 2

ANALYSING YOUR COLOURING

Over 40 years ago I pioneered the Tonal Concept, based on research that had been carried out on the artistic, scientific and commercial applications of colour. Just as the early pioneers found Newton's colour wheel inadequate to represent the many aspects of colour, I found that the available systems were insufficiently specialized or individual. I set about devising a system that would enable everyone to analyse their personal colouring accurately, and find the colours that suited them most.

Briefly, the Tonal Concept is based on 12 different colour wheels:

- **Light/Muted**
- **Muted/Light**
- **Light/Bright**
- **Bright/Light**
- **Dark/Muted**
- **Muted/Dark**
- **Dark/Bright**
- **Bright/Dark**
- **Warm/Dark**
- **Warm/Light**
- **Cool/Dark**
- **Cool/Light**

This chapter takes you step by step through a comprehensive personal-colour analysis. The results are remarkably accurate, given that the analysis is so easy to do. The following information will show you how to relate your hair, skin and eye colour to one or two of the wheels described above, which will reveal the colours that work best for you. Armed with this information, you can make the best choices of clothes and cosmetics.

Genetic Colouring

Your personal colouring is determined by your genes. The colour of your skin, hair and eyes is controlled by the amount and type of the pigment melanin present.

If your ancestors are native to hot, sunny equatorial or tropical regions, you will have inherited a great deal of melanin which naturally colours and protects your dark-looking skin, hair and eyes. If your ancestors are native to warm, sunny, sub-tropical or Mediterranean regions, you will have inherited a moderate amount of melanin. Your hair, skin and eyes will be slightly toned-down, and you will develop a moderately dark tan. If, however, your ancestors are native to cooler, less sunny, temperate regions, you will have inherited much less of the pigment eumelanin in your light, clear skin, hair and eyes and your skin will burn if exposed to excessive sunlight without protection.

Finding Your Colouring

Once you understand how light works it becomes a relatively simple matter to evaluate your own colouring. You can use this knowledge to put a personal wardrobe together, which will save you time and money, in addition to helping you overcome the problem of having lots of clothes and 'nothing to wear'.

Firstly, you need to measure how light, medium or dark you are. To do this, you will need a mirror and good daylight, preferably north-facing and not in sunlight or artificial light. You will also need to use the colour scales on pages 10–11.

Begin with your hair. Hold the hair scale at the side of your hair (see page 11) and, looking into the mirror, assess which hair sample is closest to your own hair colour. In other words, which one blends and does not stand out? Begin by eliminating what you are obviously not, and concentrate on what you might be, then pick the nearest. This will be accompa-

nied by a letter – N (neutral), Y (yellow) or R (red) – and a number – between 1 and 18 – which reflects how dark or light your hair is (1 is the lightest, 18 is the darkest).

Now turn to the colour analysis form (see page 11). Place the relevant letter in the appropriately numbered box. If, for example, your results are 'R' and 14, you would write the letter 'R' in the box numbered 14 along the hair scale.

Next, hold the skin scale close to your face (if you are sporting a tan or have uneven colouring on your face, test the neck area under your chin). Looking into the mirror, discount any colours that look closer to the mirror than your skin colour does. This should leave one or two colours that closely match your skin. Pick out the nearest, and place N, Y or R in the appropriately numbered box.

Finally, there are 36 different eye colours to choose from. These have been divided into two scales – muted and bright. Find the sample nearest to your eye colour, using the same method as for hair and skin. If the colour you have chosen is muted, then tick the appropriately numbered box along the muted scale. If it is a bright colour, tick the relevant box on the bright scale.

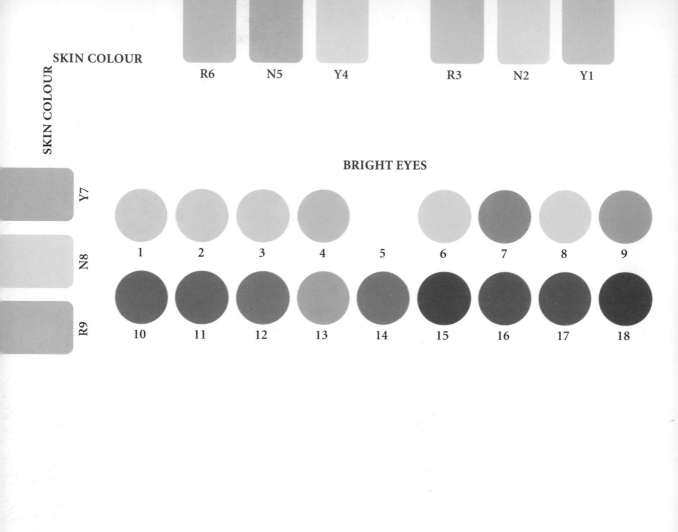

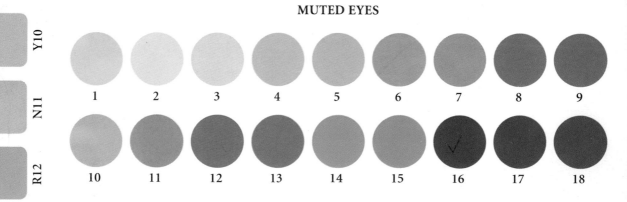

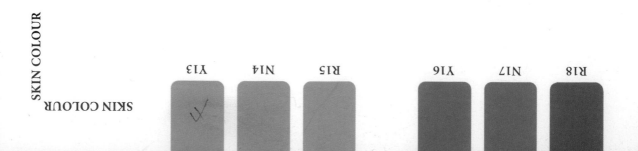

SKIN COLOUR

R6 N5 Y4 R3 N2 Y1

Y7 N8 R9

BRIGHT EYES

1 2 3 4 5 6 7 8 9

10 11 12 13 14 15 16 17 18

MUTED EYES

Y10 N11 R12

1 2 3 4 5 6 7 8 9

10 11 12 13 14 15 16 17 18

SKIN COLOUR

SKIN COLOUR

Y13 N14 R15 Y16 N17 R18

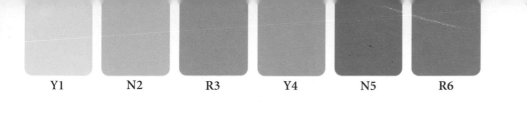

Y1 N2 R3 Y4 N5 R6

Y7
N8
R9
Y10
N11
R12

	Light									Dark								
Scale Value	1	2	3	4	5	6	7	8	9	10	11	12	13	14	15	16	17	18
Hair			R		N													
Skin			R								N		Y	N				
Eyes (muted)															✓			
Eyes (bright)																		

Y13 N14 R15 Y16 N17 R18

Finding Your Colour Wheel

The simple exercises described above give you all the information you need to pinpoint your colour wheel quickly and easily. Simply answer the following questions, and turn to the relevant page to discover which colours work best for you.

Section 1
1) **How many letters did you place in the squares numbered 1–9?** 🔲
2) **How many letters did you place in the squares numbered 10–18?** 🔲
3) **Did you come up with the same letter for your skin and hair type? If so, place that letter in the box.** ☐

Before you go on, look at your answer to question 3. If you have placed the letter 'N' in the box – or if you have left it blank – you should proceed to section 2, below. If you placed the letter 'R' or 'Y' in the box, proceed to section 3, below.

Both sections 2 and 3 will lead you to your colour wheel. Please note, however, that section 2 will lead you to two closely related colour wheels, such as light/muted and muted/light, which can be found on opposite pages. In section 3, however, you will be directed to one colour wheel only. The reason for this is that people using section 2 will have more mixed colouring than those using section 3.

Section 2
Important – use this section only if you have placed the letter 'N' in the box next to question 3, above, or if you have left it blank. The following list leads you to your colour wheel.

A) **If two or more of your chosen squares are in the 'light' half of the scale (between 1 and 9), and if you have muted eyes, choose the light/muted and muted/light colour wheels on page 13–14.**

B) **If two or more of your chosen squares are in the light half of the scale (between 1 and 9), and if you have bright eyes, choose the light/bright and bright/light colour wheels on page 16–17.**

C) **If two or more of your chosen squares are in the dark half of the scale (between 10 and 18), and if you have muted eyes, choose the dark/muted and muted/dark colour wheels on page 18–19.** ✓

D) **If two or more of your chosen squares are in the dark half of the scale (between 10 and 18), and if you have bright eyes, choose the dark/bright and bright/dark colour wheels on page 20–21.**

Section 3
Important – use this section only if you have placed the letter 'R' or 'Y' in the box

next to question 3, above. The following list leads you to your colour wheel.

A) **If two of your chosen squares are marked with the letter 'Y', and you have dark eyes, choose the Warm/Dark colour wheel on page 22.**
B) **If two of your chosen squares are marked with the letter 'Y', and you have light eyes, choose the Warm/Light colour wheel on page 23.**
C) **If two of your chosen squares are marked with the letter 'R', and you have dark eyes, choose the Cool/Dark colour wheel on page 24.**
D) **If two of your chosen squares are marked with the letter 'R', and you have light eyes, choose the Cool/Light colour wheel on page 25.**

When Colour Fades

Although ageing is a continuous process, its effects are of little consequence from a colour point of view unless sudden or serious illness is experienced, bringing about premature ageing. If you have reached middle age, however, you will know that your colouring is not what it was in your teens. The colour of your hair, skin and eyes fades as they lose their intensity and bloom. Knowing the colour area you belong to before your colouring fades will help you identify the colour changes taking place.

A person with the bright/dark and dark/bright wheels will fade towards cool/dark. A person with the bright/light and light/bright wheels will fade towards cool/light as some of the warmth and depth is lost. A person with the dark/ muted and muted/dark wheels will lose depth of colour. Any person who falls into the warm, muted or dark scales will become more muted as some of the warmth and depth is lost. Any muted colouring will become softer and lighter with age.

If all or most of your hair has gone grey with no ivory white, yellow or red showing, it means that your hair has lost or is losing most of its pigmentation. What you are seeing is light being transmitted, perhaps with a little of it being absorbed. Your skin and eyes may have taken on a greyer, softer or more clouded appearance. Your personal colouring, which you have enjoyed for many years, will be changing to a cooler, slightly softer or lighter colouring.

As well as occurring naturally, a colour change can be deliberate – such as when you decide to alter your hair colour. Whenever a colour change occurs, have a good, clear photograph taken which is the size of the inner circle of your colour wheel. Note the changes carefully. Decide whether or not your personal colouring has changed sufficiently to warrant you changing to another colour wheel.

The Complete
Colour,
Style & Image
Book

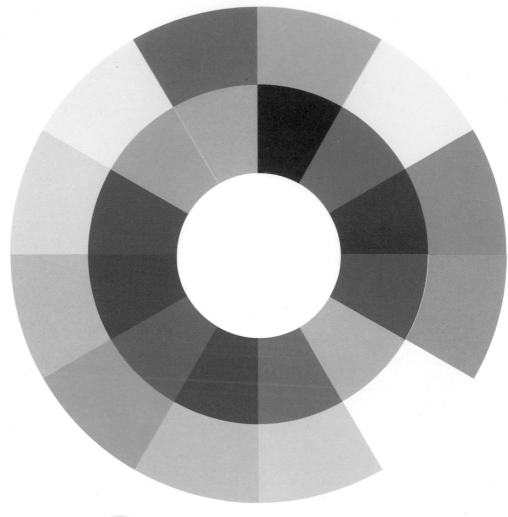

LIGHT/MUTED

MUTED/LIGHT

*The Complete
Colour,
Style & Image
Book*

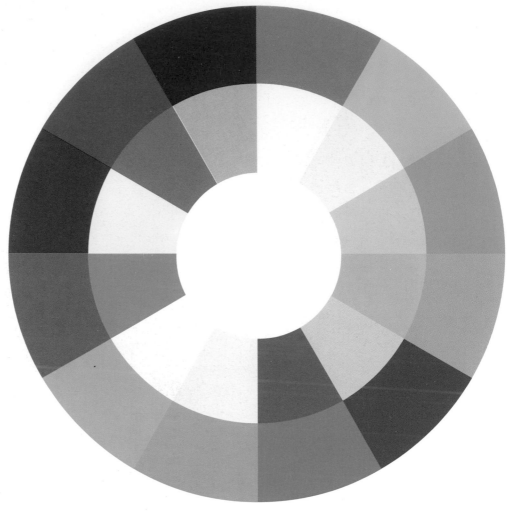

LIGHT/BRIGHT

BRIGHT/LIGHT

The Complete
Colour,
Style & Image
Book

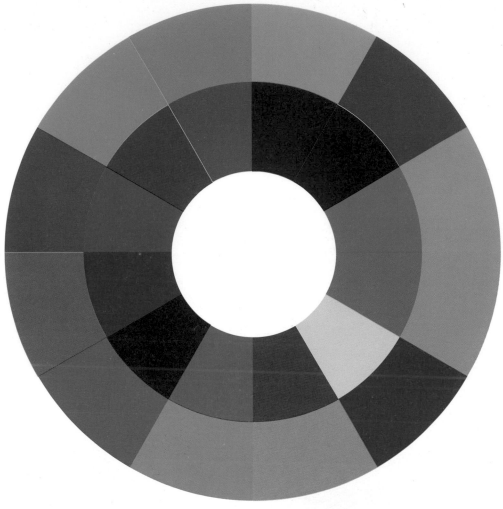

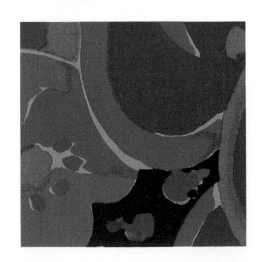

DARK/MUTED

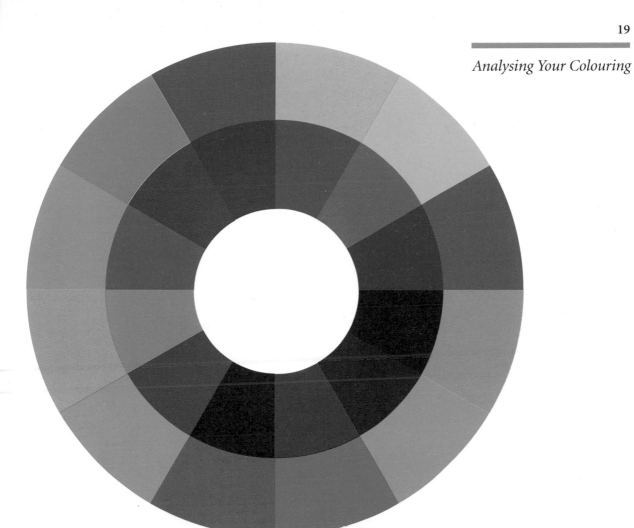

MUTED/DARK

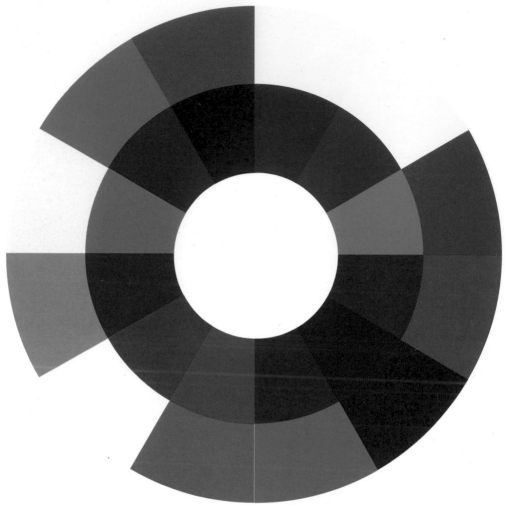

DARK/BRIGHT

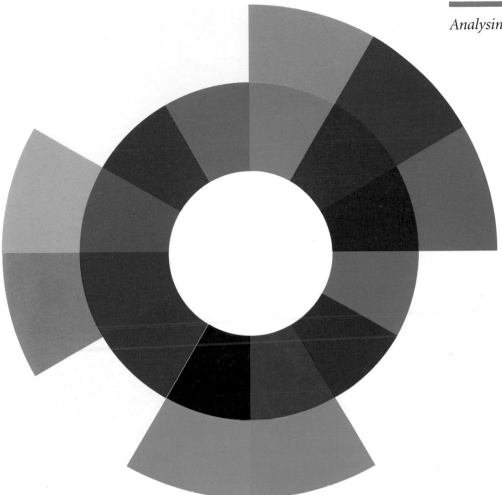

BRIGHT/DARK

The Complete Colour, Style & Image Book

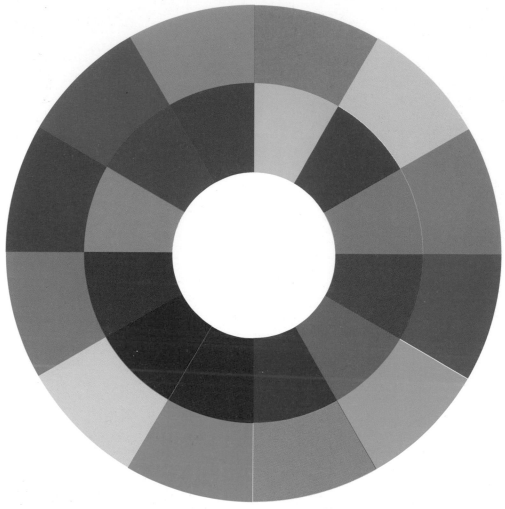

WARM/DARK

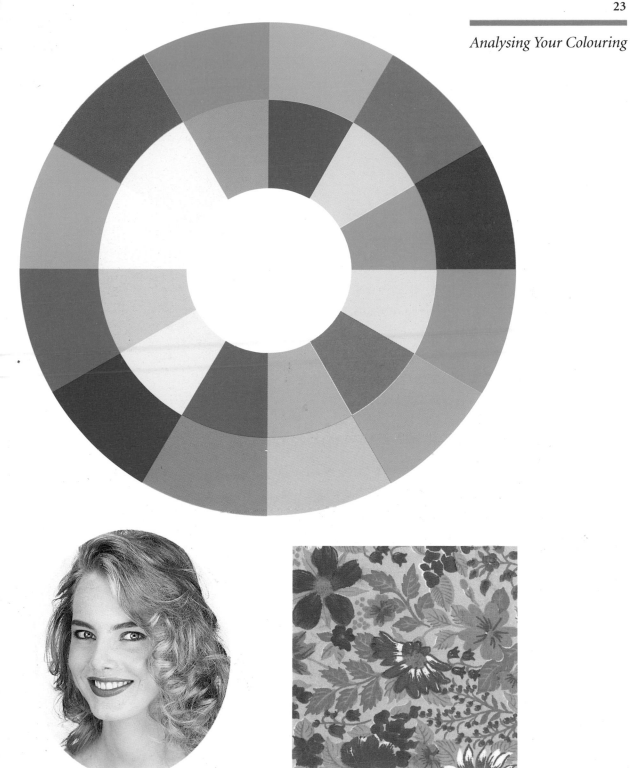

WARM/LIGHT

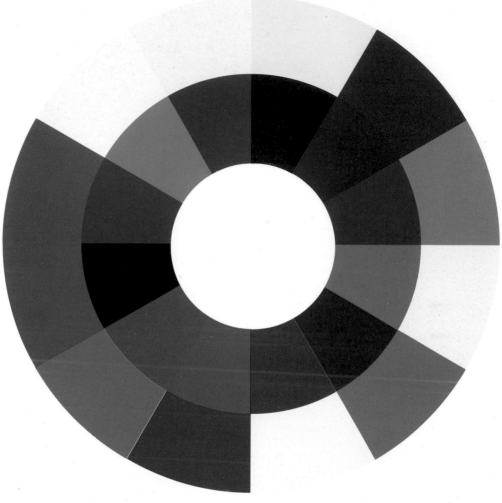

COOL/DARK

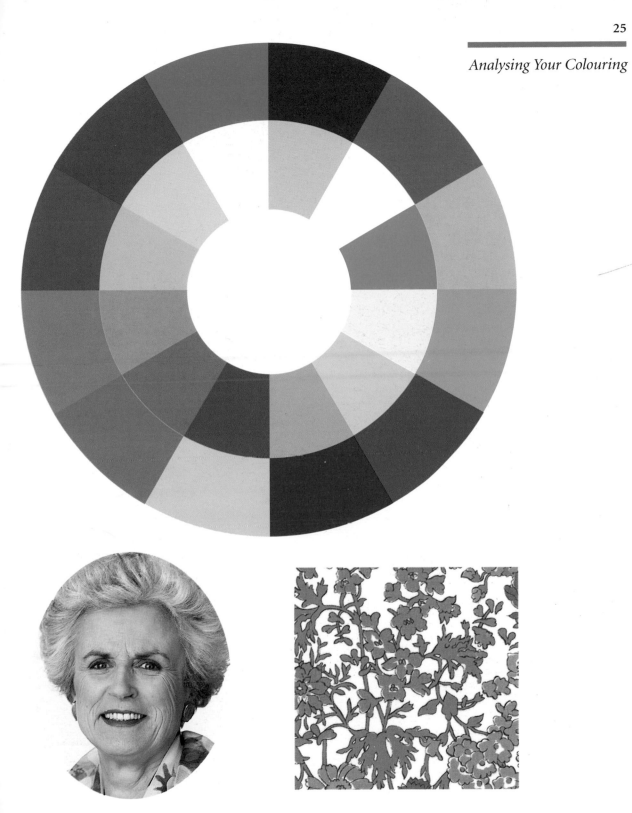

COOL/LIGHT

Using Your Wheel

The wheel's name (e.g. muted/dark) describes not only your colouring, but also the colour combinations you can wear best. You will notice that a fabric sample is given next to each wheel. These Liberty prints are meant to show you what some of your colours look like together, and how you can combine colours best.

A person with the dark/muted and muted/dark colour wheels, for example, could wear brown or mahogony with black and taupe to soften its impact, and give a very soft, sophisticated appearance.

A person with the dark/bright and bright/dark wheels person needs a sharper contrast and could wear white and red with black. This combination would, however, look too loud for the dark/muted, muted/dark person.

Now that you have identified your colour wheel, you can use the information to make the best choices every time you put together an outfit. From head to toe – make-up to shoes – you will be able to select and blend colours that work hard to make you look your best at all times. As you progress through the rest of the book, you will find it very useful to refer back to your colour wheel.

Chapter 3

BODY SHAPE

Knowing how to make the most of your figure is what fashion sense is all about. This involves carefully choosing styles that accentuate your good points and conceal your not-so-good ones. Once you have taken time to understand how to do this, looking great becomes easy. This chapter explains how you can easily discover which body type belongs to you, and then how best to dress to complement your figure.

What Body Type Are You?

To determine your body shape you need to consider:

- **your height**
- **your frame**
- **the widest and narrowest points of your body and their relationship to each other.**

Before you can become fashion-wise, you first have to become figure-wise, so this is the time for complete honesty between you and your mirror. Use a full-length mirror to examine your figure. Commence with your shoulder bone (which you will find immediately above the crease of your armpit) and visualize a vertical line running straight down your body from your armpit crease. Is your body on a parallel line all the way down, or does any part fall inside or outside the vertical line? You may find it helpful to hang a plumb line from the crease of your armpit.

The angular body shape.

The heart body shape.

To build up a complete profile of your body shape, work through the following steps. At the end of each step, record your findings. Soon you will be able to combine this knowledge with optical illusions to give you the solutions to any of your figure's imbalances.

Overall Shape

First, determine which of the basic body shapes types refers to you.

ANGULAR

You are angular if your body appears broader above the waist than below it, and you have straight, broad, sometimes bony shoulders with the rest of your body falling at a rectangular slope to the waist.

HEART

Like the angular body shape, the heart-shaped body is wider above the waist than below. This time, however, the upper forearms look wider than the shoulders, with the bust coming close to or over-hanging the imaginary plumb line.

The curvy pear body
shape.

The straight pear body
shape.

The straight body
shape – with a waist.

The straight body
shape.

The curvy ellipse body
shape.

The straight ellipse
body shape.

The balanced hourglass
body shape.

The curvy hourglass
body shape.

PEAR

If your body hangs over the imaginary plumb line below the waist, with the upper part of your body staying inside the line, then you are pear-shaped. If your thighs hang over more than your hips you are a straight pear, whereas if your thighs and hips hang over equally you are a curvy pear.

ELLIPSE

Your shape can be described as an ellipse if your body runs parallel with the imaginary plumb line from your bust area down to your hips and then slopes inwards to a slimmer thigh area. If your shoulders are narrow in comparison to your waist, making your waist seem high or non-existent, then you are a straight ellipse. You are a curvy ellipse if extra weight has accumulated around your waist making it hang over the imaginary plumb line between your bust and hip area, and you have very little or no waistline.

HOURGLASS

This body profile is considered to be the feminine ideal. You are a balanced hourglass if you display a slim waistline and are proportionately curvy above and below the waist, even if you hang over the plumb line at your bust and hips. If extra weight has accumulated across your bust, upper forearms, waist and hips, then you are a curvy hourglass.

STRAIGHT

A straight body shape is balanced above and below the waist and in line all the way down the imaginary plumb line. This body profile can be narrow-boned and rectangular, or broader and squarer. Alternatively, it can look like two stacked squares, revealing a waist and a rectangular appearance. This profile generally has very little waist, although there are exceptions to this rule.

Height

A female body between 5'4" (1.63 m) and 5'6" (1.68 m) is considered of average height. Under 5'4" (1.63 m) and you are considered shorter than average. Over 5'6" (1.68 m) or taller and you are considered taller than average.

Neck

To discover whether your neck is short, average or long, put on a top with a mandarin neckline or turtle collar, and then look in the mirror. If your neck is of average length, there will be as much neck showing above the collar as there is hidden by the collar. If you have a long neck, there will be twice as much or more neck showing than there is hidden.

Shoulders

Visual proportion is the relationship between various parts of your body and how they compare with one another. In a visually balanced body, your shoulders should appear to be the widest part of your body by 1–1½ inches (2.5–4 cm) from the bone at the top of the spinal column to the height at the top of the shoulder. Measure your shoulder 'drop' to find your shoulder type:

0–1 inch (0–2.5 cm) indicates very straight shoulders
1–1½ inches (2.5–4 cm) indicates straight shoulders
2–2½ inches (5–6.5 cm) indicates tapered shoulders
Above 2½ inches (6.5 cm) indicates sloped shoulders

Arms

You usually know without measuring whether you have slim, average or heavy arms.

Wrists

Your wristbone generally determines the size of your body frame. A wrist measurement of:

5–5½ inches (13–14 cm) indicates a small frame
5½–6 inches (14–15 cm) indicates a medium frame

6–6½ inches (15–16.5 cm) or over indicates a large frame

Waist

An average waist is one which falls halfway between the round bone at the top of your spine and the bone at the base of your spine. Your elbow usually falls where your waist should be.

Hips

If you have straight hips, your waist measurement will be between 0–5 inches (0–13 cm) of your hip size. If you have sloping hips, the measurement will vary from the waist by approximately 5–7 inches (13–18 cm). Curvy hips are indicated by a waist measurement between 7 and 10 inches (18–25 cm) of the hip size.

Bottom

Viewed from the side, does your bottom look flat, protruding only as much as your back above the waist? Does your bottom gradually slope outwards, or have you got a curvy bottom commencing almost immediately below the waist?

Legs

Are your legs short, balanced or long? In order for your legs to look balanced, the distance from your crotch to the floor should appear as long as, or longer than, the distance from the top of your head to your crotch.

Body Balance

You can find out how balanced, or in proportion, your body is by looking at where certain points fall in relation to your height. The ideal is when your waist falls halfway between your shoulder line and your bottom (roughly where your elbow is). If your waist is higher than the midpoint, you are short-waisted. If lower, you are long-waisted.

Regardless of weight and height, a visually balanced figure always looks better than an unbalanced one. For the majority of people who do not have a perfectly balanced figure, there are ways in which an illusion of balance can be created. To be able to do this, you need to understand the concept of 'line'. This term refers to the outline of a garment and the style lines within it that divide it up. A line will lead the eye and can be used to create an optical illusion similar to that of colour. A balanced visual effect is achieved by correct proportioning.

Lines and shapes have expressive and aesthetic qualities creating the finished effect. For example, a dress comprizing sharp, straight lines will not work with a curvy, shaped jacket. And a dress of restrained curves is seen as more feminine than one whose lines are straight or diagonal.

Clothes should impart a sense of unison to your body. If all the dress lines work together in harmony they create an attractive visual effect. Creating uniformity in an outfit demands that the style and seam lines of clothing covering the top half of your body align with those on your bottom half. All areas of dress should reflect the same shapes. The lines and design features should be organized with rhythm and a graceful, flowing movement to lead the eyes towards a feature you wish to emphasize. It should not be static or disjointed.

To know what a line can or cannot do has to become instinctive before you can be really creative. The only way to devel-

Holding this illustration in front of you, ask yourself where your eyes rest. You will discover that this will always be on the widest bar. Exactly the same thing happens when you look at a person walking in front of you. Your eyes will always settle on the widest part of their body. This, if nothing else, is an excellent reason for wearing shoulder pads if your shoulders are not the widest part of your body.

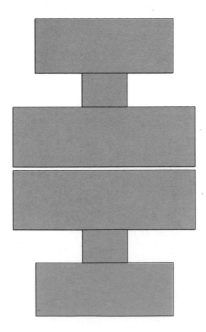

op your instincts for line is through practice. The following guidelines, which look at how line can be used to complement your figure, will give you a good basis on which to start experimenting with line.

Shoulders

The human eye easily accepts a body shape or garment silhouette which is symmetrical and balanced. It will even correct and skim over slight discrepancies in size and shape. It is only when there is a part of the body which does not balance with the rest that it draws attention to it.

In order for your body to look well-balanced, the shoulders must be perceived as the widest part of your body. This has to be borne in mind when considering the hang of your clothes.

Waistlines

TO BALANCE A SHORT WAIST
- **Wear a belt which is the same colour as your top.**
- **Choose a coloured top which you can blouson over a contrasting bottom, giving the impression of a lower waistline.**
- **Choose dresses with tapered skirts, with either a drop-waisted style or no waist detail.**

TO BALANCE A LONG WAIST
- **Wear a belt the same colour as your skirt or trousers.**

- **Choose designs that give the illusion of a higher waist, such as skirts with broad waistbands.**
- **Choose designs that miss the waist and emphasize other parts of the body.**

Jacket and Tunic Length

The length of your jacket, tunic or sweater is a very important horizontal line because it can make the bottom half of your body look very imbalanced. Always check in a full-length mirror that you have it right for you. If your jacket or tunic is long, try wearing it with a short skirt, or a long skirt with a belt around the jacket. Ask yourself which length helps to balance your shape and size. Many people make their legs look too short because they do not take into consideration the length of their over-blouse or tunic.

Look at the jacket designs shown (on page 32), and note the different hemlines.

Three lengths of tunic. Which one is right for you?

A selection of jacket styles. The jackets with cut-away hemlines would give length to the skirt and make the legs look longer. The hemlines that create an unbroken horizontal line can make the legs look shorter.

Hemlines and Skirts

The skirt length influences your entire body proportions. When choosing the right hemline for you, consider your figure, legs and fashion preferences. By looking at the different styles of skirts shown (below), you can see for yourself which style draws your eye to different parts of the skirt and, therefore, the body.

Your hemline is a horizontal line that attracts attention, especially if the colour line is broken. Loud and contrasting colours at this point do not just get attention, they grab it. Make sure, then, that this is a flattering area to draw attention to, and that your height can stand being shortened. To avoid attracting attention to this area, wear hose and hemline in a neutral or close-intensity colour. For example, choose a navy skirt with grey tights of the same intensity. To attract attention to this area, wear contrasting hose and hemline colours.

Skirt hemlines can add or take away inches from your height, so always check your total look. To find the most flattering hemline position for you, take a towel, view yourself in a full-length mirror and move it up and down your legs. As a general rule you will find that the best length will be just above or just below the thickest part of the leg, except for someone who has very thin legs. You should always wear lengths at or around the thickest part of your leg, with slight adjustments up or down if your legs can take it.

Evaluate total proportion and balance in relation to your figure. Low-heeled shoes with matching hose – or neutral hose in the same intensity – and a short hemline will create a good balance. Short skirts balance a long jacket. A medium shoe heel adds to the illusion of height and is the most versatile. Boots can create length provided that the skirt covers the boots with no leg showing.

A selection of skirt styles.

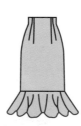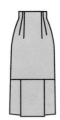

Line Design

Most woman want their clothes to adorn and balance their body shape and to maximize or minimize their height or width. This is where colour and line work together synergistically to provide the key principles of clothes-design aesthetics. By becoming aware of what line design in clothing will or will not do, you can make your visual image taller, shorter, fatter or thinner. You should take the onlooker's eye to a good area of your body that can stand to be scrutinized, and away from an area that cannot.

These principles do not change. Once you are familiar with them and know what they are capable of doing, you will find it simple to make choices of clothing style and pattern that will flatter your body shape and colouring.

Vertical Lines

When vertical lines are used on a dress or outfit, less attention is focused on the outline of the figure as the eye is busy fol-

Which of the following lines looks the shortest? Which looks the longest? Which falls in-between? You will probably find that lines

1 and 4 look the shortest, line 2 looks the longest and line 3 falls in-between. All the lines are, in fact, the same length.

lowing the vertical line. The vertical line gives the illusion of height and it can also be used to divide the figure, making it appear thinner.

Horizontal Lines

Horizontal lines widen and shorten, but when carefully used they can be a very effective styling device, as they attract the onlooker's attention to a part of your body you wish to emphasize or bring into balance. Used at the waist and hemline, horizontal lines can dramatically change the visual proportions of your upper and lower body.

These three examples are the same width, but the one in the middle appears wider because it has a horizontal line at the waist.

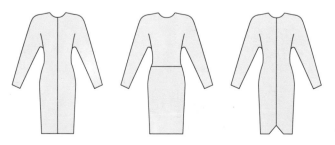

The Complete Colour, Style & Image Book

LEFT: Horizontal lines lengthen, shorten, widen, narrow and attract the eye.

 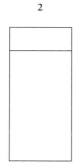  

1   2   3   4

ABOVE: Which of the rectangles looks the longest? Although they are all the same size, rectangle 4 gives the greatest illusion of length. Notice how the short-waisted rectangle 2 appears to be the second-longest. The divide in rectangle 1 is where you would expect to see the waistline. The low-waisted rectangle 3 looks the shortest.

Curvy Lines

Extreme curvy lines exaggerate size, while more gentle curves are graceful, feminine and create the impression of a smooth figure.

ABOVE: Examples of styles with gentle curves.

ABOVE: When diagonal lines converge, they focus attention on the area to which they narrow.

Diagonal Lines

Diagonal lines are dynamic and attract attention to detail. The more vertical a diagonal line, the taller and slimmer you will look.

BELOW: Converging diagonal lines can emphasize the waist.

BELOW: Converging lines make a dress look longer and narrower.

Diverging lines make a dress look shorter and wider.

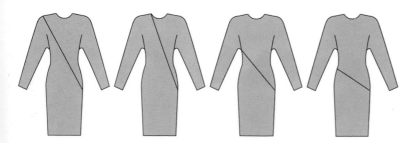 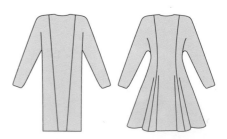

Balancing Your Body Shape by Design

This following section looks at different body types and the lines that most complement them.

Heart

Straight

Angular

Ellipse

Pear

Hourglass

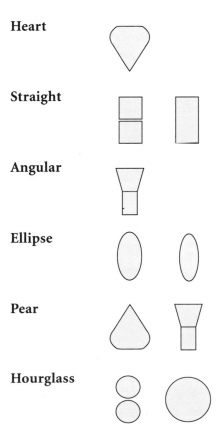

Colour and Line Synergy

As we have now seen, a line which leads the eye can create an optical illusion in much the same way as colour does. Add these two elements of design together with correct proportioning and you can visually balance a figure shape to such an extent that no one will ever guess that your figure shape is less than perfectly proportioned. Here are some guidelines for using both line and colour to great effect for each figure type:

Heart
Shoulder pads allow the fabric to hang free and clear of the wider part of the arm. If you have accumulated extra weight down your trunk towards your waist, use a slightly looser style line with a non-advancing colour from your colour wheel for the sleeves and buttons. Centre detail and cut-in sleeves divide your upper body making it look smaller visually. If further correction is needed you could have the inside panel in a strong advancing colour or fabric design. (See the illustrations on page 38.)

*The Complete
Colour,
Style & Image
Book*

RIGHT: Shoulder pads,
creative button place-
ment through the skirt,
and the centre detail
provided by the
heart-shaped neckline
all take the eye from
the heavy forearms
and balance the heart-
shaped figure.

FAR RIGHT: In this
design, non-advancing
colours have been
placed down the outer
seams and sleeves, and
a matching eye-catch-
ing check design has
been used in the centre
to create balance.

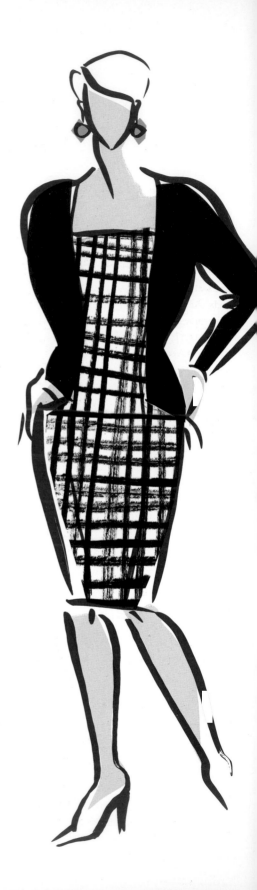

RIGHT: This tapered dress with shoulder pads, short sleeves and horizontal pockets gives width to the top half of the body, making the waist, hips and thighs look smaller and more shapely.

FAR RIGHT: If you have a broad, straight figure, the clever use of colour in patterns can focus attention on selected areas of the body as well as making it look slimmer. The design shown here is ideal.

Straight

Shoulder pads can be used to balance a tunic or dress in a semi-fitted A-line. This will give you a feminine swing and bring balance to your figure shape.

RIGHT: A low-yoke
design with sleeves and
yoke picked out in a
non-advancing colour
will take the focus
away from your
shoulders. If you
are tall, it will mini-
mize your shoulders
and height.

FAR RIGHT: Unusual
line-design features
and fabric mixes can
focus the eye to the
centre, away from the
broad shoulders.

Angular

If you have an angular figure you have an
imbalance with the bottom half of your
body, but unlike the heart shaped figure
you have straight lines which are perceived as being rather masculine. The
object is to bring the two extremes closer
together.

Pear

If you are a true pear shape you will be at least one size smaller on the top half of your body than you are on the bottom half. Using shoulder pads and a light colour on the top half will visually give you more width and make your waist appear smaller. Wearing dark and subdued colours on the bottom half will minimize your thigh area. A dress with a low, curved, dropped waist is another good choice, as this emphasizes your smooth waistline.

Wearing white with a black background leads the eye away from the thicker areas of the thigh. The white in the jacket is expansive, making the top half of the body look wider, thereby creating balance. The cut-away jacket breaks up the horizontal line and gives length to the bottom half.

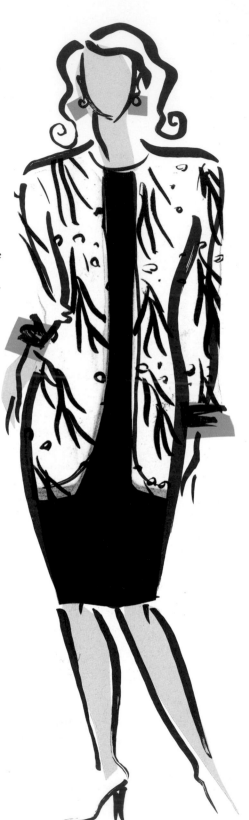

RIGHT: A good example of plain and patterned fabrics working together to enhance the straight ellipse figure. The curvy ellipse figure could wear this by reversing the fabrics – a plain jacket over a patterned dress, for example.

FAR RIGHT: Diagonal lines placed across the low waist to the thigh area on a tapered skirt creates an eye-catching, flattering look.

Ellipse

If you have an ellipse figure your objectives must be to widen your shoulders visually with shoulder pads and line design, to bypass your waist and to emphasize your wonderfully shaped thighs and legs. Choose a yoke to create width, centred buttons for interest, and a tapered skirt to add to the line.

This outfit is an excellent choice for the curvy figure. Semi-fitted with shoulder pads, it gives smooth emphasis to the waist and thighs. The dark skirt balances a heavy bottom, particularly as the skirt colour is incorporated into the top half.

Hourglass

A successful look for this figure type is a dress with sleeves and outside panels in a non-advancing colour, and centre panels in an advancing colour. This gives a very slimming effect to the areas where the curvy hourglass generally puts on weight.

Fashion Guidelines

Style is something that is uniquely yours, and provides an insight into your personality. During my work as a colour consultant, I have met countless people who genuinely believed that their size presented a barrier to their style because they were severely limited in the colours and designs they could wear.

The truth is much more positive. Everyone, regardless of size, can develop a personal style that makes the most of their positive features and minimizes the negative ones. All you need to do is to keep in mind the following basic guidelines:

Average Figure

If you are of average height and size, your main concern should be to avoid designs and looks that create an imbalance, or shorten your figure. Use the same intensity colour for shoes, hose and hemline. If a

Unfussy outfits in single or harmonizing colours flatter the average figure.

colour break is desirable for a change, choose colours which are close in intensity or which will be carried upwards in a pattern or check design.

- **Always match or tone shoe and hose colours to your hemline colour to lengthen your legs.**
- **Select neutral and basic colours for business wear.**
- **Wear colours which are close in colour value, such as a mono look, from head to foot. Match shoe and hose colours to outside and/or inside garment colours.**
- **A short or long coat can add a contrasting colour effect.**
- **A contrasting jacket should finish in the area between your natural waist and above your full hip.**
- **Choose designs with vertical lines, and jackets with a cut-a-way at the hemline. This gives centre interest and a longer look to the skirt.**
- **Avoid hemline patterns and frills or any straight horizontal lines from the hipline downwards.**
- **Avoid overwhelming detail such as extra large collars and belts; oversized sleeves; big, bold prints; bulky fabric; too many colour breaks; excessive fullness; and garments that are too long.**

Short, Broad Figure

Your main concern should be to avoid designs and looks which create an imbalance and shorten your figure. Always remember that a horizontal line will shorten, add width to your body and attract attention. Bulky fabric also adds width and can visually shorten your look, as can skirts which have a lot of volume or weight in the fabric.

The following guidelines will visually make a person with this figure type look-taller and slimmer:

- **Use a mono look from head to toe (shoes, hose and dress) or add a contrasting colour at the neckline.**
- **Keeping shoes, hose, skirt and jacket in one of your best neutral colours, add a multicoloured blouse in a lightweight fabric in your best basic colour.**
- **Keeping shoes, hose and dress in the same colour, add another colour in your jacket, cardigan or coat.**
- **Tapered skirts give length to your look.**
- **Jackets with a cut-a-way at the hemline create centre interest and a longer look to the skirt.**
- **Balance head size with a soft, medium-volume hair style.**
- **To look taller and narrower, avoid fitted curvy lines, too much fullness, too many details, large fussy sleeves,** horizontal stripes, heavy-looking fabrics and over use of colour breaks which create straight, horizontal lines.

Create a contrasting centre panel or centre detail with a frill, buttons or piping running vertically down the garment. Alternatively, use vertical, asymmetrical designs and two-tone colouring.

You can add inches to your height by directing the eye upwards towards the face. To do this choose vertical lines in design or style. You could, for example, wear one colour from top to toe, perhaps with a colour break near the neckline.

Short, Petite Figure

This figure shape is generally an underdeveloped version of a straight, curved, pear or ellipse type. You should follow the guidelines given for the figure shape you most closely resemble, choosing designs that give you height and avoiding anything that overwhelms you.

Your main concern should be to avoid designs and looks which make you look too schoolgirlish or create an imbalance and visually shorten your image even more. Take care when balancing long sweaters and jackets as all horizontal lines and colour breaks will create a shortening effect if they appear too severe. Fussiness around the hemline or contrasting colours, say in footwear or tights, will attract the eye downwards making you visibly lose inches. Stay away from bulky and heavy fabrics – they have nothing in common with your look.

A loose- fitting bodice (blouson-style top) worn over a flared skirt gives balance to the tall, thin figure.

Tall, Thin Figure

Colour breaks and horizontal lines all help to create width, and loose-fitting garments distract attention from your height. Follow these guidelines to get the most from your figure:

- **Use shoulder pads to help create a waist (if necessary).**
- **Heavy fabric for skirts can add width, but can overwhelm your bone structure by making your arms and legs look skinny, and can create an appearance of being too heavy for the body it is on.**
- **Add a belt to pick up the colour of your skirt or blouse to create another break. Large, decorative belts are particularly suitable.**
- **Jackets with a straight hemline give a horizontal line.**
- **To create interest at the neck area, use a contrasting colour for a collar or deep yoke.**
- **Wedge styles create interest. They can bring some fullness to a tailored or semi-tailored look.**
- **Avoid straight, vertical lines, a mono look, clingy designs and fabric.**
- **Balance head size with a soft, medium- volume hairstyle.**

Any of the following styles are suitable for this figure shape:

- **Double-breasted jackets worn with light-to-medium or neutral hose to create a break in colour between your shoes and your hemline, as the more horizontal lines there are in an outfit, the shorter the body will look. If you add colour breaks that create horizontal lines, this will exaggerate the effect.**
- **Separates that coordinate and create a suit look.**
- **Patterned dresses with dirndl skirt styles and double-breasted cardigans or vests.**
- **Neutral suits with patterned blouses.**
- **Check or plaid suit jackets with plain skirts.**
- **Pleated, plaid or check skirts with one colour taken up into your blouse. A second colour can then be picked out for your jacket, belt and shoes.**
- **Multi-coloured tops ending at the hip or below to create one horizontal line.**
- **Full, soft blouses and dresses.**
- **Long jackets – the taller you are the longer your jackets can be.**
- **Flared and draped skirts.**
- **Yokes with gathers.**
- **Skirts with pockets.**
- **Loose, crossover designs.**

Tall, Broad Figure

This figure shape benefits from wearing a clever mixture of colours. Be careful, however, not to end one colour and start a contrasting one on a part of your body you would rather camouflage, as this will create more width. You will find the following guidelines helpful:

- **Select designs with vertical lines, or lines that close asymmetrically. These have a slimming effect and create interest.**
- **Choose simple styles with enough fabric to allow easy movement. Remember, however, that too much fullness and a bulky fabric makes a large person look even larger.**
- **Choose loose-fitting, semi-fitted or flared garments.**
- **Break up vertical lines on the top half of the body by wearing more than one colour.**
- **Pick out one of the darker or more subdued colours from your top and use it as a block colour for your bottom half.**
- **Choose a one-piece dress with a big collar in a contrasting colour which extends down the middle.**
- **Use deep yokes, providing your bust line can stand them.**
- **Choose a seven-eighths-length jacket which tapers slightly towards your hemline over a matching or**

A mixture of vertical and horizontal lines focuses the eye up towards the face and to the centre of the body. The outline tapers gradually from the shoulders to the hemline to give shape and balance.

contrasting multi-coloured dress or suit.

- Jackets with a straight hemline create a horizontal line where they end.
- Use diagonal and asymmetrical lines with two-tone colouring.
- Wear elasticated waistbands for comfort.
- Have a middle panel in a different colour to your side panels and sleeves.
- Wear the sleeves, yoke and tapered skirt in one colour and the main body of a three-quarter-length, tapering tunic in another contrasting or harmonious colour.
- Avoid lines that arc too curved or have too much fullness, and small design details which will appear out of proportion.
- Also avoid clingy fabric, fussy sleeves, horizontal stripes and short jackets.
- Balance head size with a soft, medium-volume hairstyle.

Chapter 4

COLOUR AND STYLE

Most people can choose a simple colour that looks good on them, but few of us can combine colours that make us look especially attractive, or choose colours that are appropriate for our lifestyle. Many of the rules we followed in the past for colour combinations no longer apply, such as 'blue with green should never be seen' and 'orange and pink stink'. There is always an exception to the rule and it is easier to be creative within the colour ranges of your colour wheels.

This chapter looks at how you can wear the colours in your wheel to best effect. It describes what happens to colours when they are worn together, and suggests good combinations. It also provides guidelines for putting together a complete lifestyle wardrobe, and describes the different 'looks' available, from classic to casual.

Colour Preferences

In stating a preference for a colour, your choice is often dictated by circumstances. If your choice is unrestricted, then it will be determined not only by your psychological preferences, but also by aesthetic considerations such as whether a dress will go with your colouring and make-up to create the desired effect, and what it does for your body shape. Broadly speaking, most people are unaware of the real power colour plays in their lives, even though most of us would admit to having felt the difference colour can make. We

choose to ignore what our bodies are telling us.

The psychological side to colour in dress cannot be totally ignored, however, as it relates to our personal feelings of wellbeing. You should not always wear colours because they *look* best on you, but because you *feel* best in them for your present mood.

Choosing Colours

Whatever your intended image – sophisticated, businesslike or sporty, for example – knowing your colour wheels and levels of contrast will help you look your best. You cannot wear all the colours of your wheels equally well, so you must know how to wear them to create different looks and moods. You should also bear in mind that colour combinations which work well for some wheel types do not work so well for others. Those with bright colour wheels, for example, always

look best in colour combinations that create a bright and contrasting look in line with their personal colouring. Appropriate selections from the colour wheel might be red, white and navy. The opposite applies for those with muted colour wheel types, who might select teal, light taupe, beige and navy, for example.

Every wheel has its own set of advancing and non-advancing colours, and the rules outlined in Chapter 1 should be taken into consideration. If you want to wear an advancing colour but do not want to put yourself too much on show, you must give less space to the advancing colours and more space to the non-advancing colours.

Keeping in mind the name of your wheels will help you recognize your best colour combinations. For example, bright/dark looks best in bright/dark combinations, such as navy and emerald. If you want to add colour intensities which do not appear on your colour wheels, then these colours are best kept within a print, or away from the face.

Complementary colour combinations within your wheels can be too loud or dramatic when placed alongside one another. You can negate this effect by choosing one colour from a darker or lighter intensity; by reducing the space allocated to one of these colours; or by adding a third, neutral colour to act as an arbitrator (see Chapter 1, p.6).

Yellows

The yellows of most of the colour wheels require special consideration, particularly if you are not seeking immediate attention. The advancing yellow-greens of the bright, warm and muted colour wheels are difficult colours to wear in large amounts (such as chartreuse and lime-green). They are best worn in a pattern with other colours, in small amounts or as an accent to make a fashion statement. To create a slick look for warm weather, add these colours to white, periwinkle or blue-violet from your wheels. Such colour combinations can look stunning. Just be careful not to overdo it.

Greens

The true greens of the bright colour wheels can be dominant in some circumstances as, if used in large amounts, they advance at a similar speed to some reds. True green is of medium intensity with little or no undertone, which means that it is equally balanced between warm and cool. This in itself can create a problem if you put true green close to overly warm or cool colours. In effect, this colour takes on the opposite undertone to that of the colour next to which you have placed it.

Dark greens found on the dark colour wheels – such as pine and forest – can be worn as neutrals by most people in place of black when coordinated with pastel,

bright and neutral shades from their own colour wheels. The undertone of the green must be kept in tune with your personal colouring.

Green and red of the same clarity can be balanced equally in an outfit when a neutral is used to separate the two and holds the largest amount of space.

Found in the dark and muted colour wheels, olive should be treated as a neutral as it looks drab on its own for most people. Olive mixes well with most of the colours of the wheels in which it is found, and it plays down the overly brights.

Blue-greens

Blue-greens and turquoises of medium to dark intensity found on your colour wheel mix well with the monotones of your wheels. When mixed with your best white, these colours can be used to give a clean 'holiday' look. Add one of your reds if you belong to the bright to light wheels to amplify and brighten the look. Adding black or dark grey to these colours creates an office look.

Aqua, an equal mix of blue and green, is a good colour for almost everyone with its medium intensity. It has been used primarily as a sports colour, but works equally well for a smart casual or office look when teamed with darker neutrals. It is a good choice for a group of brides-maids of mixed personal colouring, as is periwinkle blue – another medium-intensity colour. When mixed with the darker greys, navys and browns, periwinkle blue creates a professional look.

Blues

Combining the blue and white of the light/bright colour wheels creates a similarly light, bright look. Add the yellow or red for an even brighter sporty or nautical look. Blues on the dark/muted and muted/dark wheels require a little more sophistication – try adding gold, mahogany or rust.

Greyed-down blues (such as French, powder and light periwinkle) are found on the muted wheels. Their grey content helps them to behave like a neutral while retaining some softness. They mix well with the light and dark neutrals and colours of your wheels, from a light taupe and soft white to a muted pink and cocoa combination.

Purples and Violets

Often worn for more sophisticated or dressy looks, purples and violets have now become popular for professional dressing. These looks can be enhanced by accessorizing with the pink, red, orange or lime-green of your wheels. A darker intensity can be worn in place of neutrals.

Burgundy and Aubergine

Burgundy and aubergine, which are a mix of reds and browns, are good colour mixers as they absorb some of the undertone of the colours with which you combine them. Black brings out their richness whereas white provides too stark a contrast. Pastel aqua, pinks, violets, light beiges and taupes all work well with these colours as do the grey, violet/purple and navy neutrals of your wheels.

Reds

Red is found on every wheel, but must be worn differently by those who fall into the bright colour wheels than by those whose wheels are muted. The colours of the bright and light-bright wheels advance. The brightest reds are the most advancing, carefree and attention-seeking of all the reds. Wearing such a red with the best white/ivory in a two-colour look lifts the red to give it a bright, fresh look. This will harmonize with your personal colouring. Adding a dark neutral from the appropriate wheel, such as black, navy, tan, brown or grey, will create a three-colour professional look. Black and navy are more advancing colours than the brown family.

Black absorbs red and has a tendency to make it look darker, so when these two colours are worn together on the top half of the body they suit those who fall into the bright/dark and dark/bright colour wheels best. Those who fall into the dark/muted, muted/dark and warm/muted/dark wheels can wear red with the full range of their colour wheel's beiges, browns, darker olives and greens for their best look. These people can also wear a mix of black, brown and red.

People with muted personal colouring feel more comfortable when the advancing colours of their wheels are balanced with the less-advancing colours. When green and violet/purple are dark enough to be worn as neutrals, red becomes a good blouse or accessory colour.

Shades of Pink

Pink, peach, salmon and lighter shades of red are softer, easier to wear and less threatening than their advancing counterparts. In a jacket or blouse they can make an old navy, grey, or black-and-white check skirt come to life. These colours are sophisticated as an accent colour to the navy, browns, and dark violet/purples of your wheels.

Black and Charcoal

Everyone can wear black and charcoal. For those whose colour wheels have light or muted in their description, large areas of black should be limited to the bottom half of the body with only a little black brought up to the top in the design or accent. The majority of people using the bright and dark/bright colour wheels can wear their black on its own for a 'mono' look, or with any of the colours and neutrals of their wheels to create contrast, such as black and white or black, white and red. Those using dark/muted, muted/dark and warm/dark wheels can wear black best in a patterned design which incorporates brown, mahogany or other neutral colours, the latter softening the black and lessening the contrast.

Navy

The navys of your wheels are the best ones for you to wear. As with black, however, if you are using the light/bright, bright/light, bright/dark or dark/bright colour wheels, then wide contrast plays its part. In such cases, contrast navy with the white, pastels and bright colours of your wheels. Those using muted/dark, dark/muted or warm/dark wheels, can contrast navy with teal, turquoise, rust and mahogany, adding the toned-down whites, beiges and light taupes of their colour wheels.

The Personality of Colour

The colours you unconsciously choose to wear are vital clues to your inner personality and can help you discover yourself.

Colours have personalities too, and knowing what they are helps you to select the right colours for the message you want to convey. Always choose colours that *feel* good on you, and are appropriate for the occasion.

Advancing and Non-advancing Colours

Advancing colours are the ones that seem to advance towards you when you hold your colour wheels up at arm's length. To be able to use colour most effectively, you need to know what the advancing and non-advancing colours are 'saying'. In the following table, the words in the left column describe the advancing colours of your colour wheels, and those in the right column describe the non-advancing ones. Each colour wheel contains colours with

ADVANCING	NON-ADVANCING
Active	Passive
Analytical	Intuitive
Animated	Quiet
Assertive	Submissive
Direct	Subtle
Dramatic	Reserved
Extrovert	Introvert
Exuberant	Calm
Forceful	Gentle
Intense	Relaxed
Realistic	Idealistic

advancing personalities and those with non-advancing ones. When combined, they create a balance and can be used to offset one another. We will discuss later how your personality is influenced by the advancing or non-advancing colours in your personal colouring.

Colour as a Design Element

When combining colours in your outfit, choose the non-advancing colours of your colour wheels for the part of the body you wish to minimize, and the advancing colours for the part of the body you wish to highlight. Red, orange, yellow and yellow-greens of any wheel will advance more than the green, blue/green, blue and violet of the same wheel.

A dark colour will always appear darker when placed near a light one. The dark colour makes the light colour look lighter, creating more of a contrast, a colour break and focal point than if it were placed alongside a colour closer in intensity. Dark colours which advance carry the most influence and convey an aura of power and authority.

If you want to express a quieter mood represented by the meanings given for non-advancing colours in the right column of the above table, then wear light-to-medium colour combinations selected from your colour wheels. If, on the other hand, you want to create a bolder look represented by the meanings given for the advancing colours in the left column, then wear together the light, medium and dark advancing colours of your wheels.

For your very best colour combinations, match your wheel intensities to your own personal colouring and contrast levels. For example, if you have dark-brown hair, medium to dark-brown/hazel eyes and medium skin colour, your best, most well-balanced colour combination would be black, mahogany and light taupe.

Body Colours and Contrast Levels

Your personal colouring affects the way in which you should combine colours. Consult the guidelines for your wheel type, below, and use the information to help you look and feel great, and be in control of the colours you wear. Study your personal colour wheels, stretch your imagination and create new combinations. Play around with various colour possibilities, draw and crayon outfits or use fabric samples to test your ideas.

> KEY
> (A) Advancing
> (LA) Less advancing
> (NA) Non-advancing.

Light/Muted
Select soft colour combinations (NA) with low-to-medium contrast.

Muted/Light
Select medium-to-light colour combinations (LA, NA) with little contrast.

Light/Bright
Select clear, medium-bright colour combinations (LA) with medium-to-sharp contrast.

Bright/Light
Select bright, clear colour combinations (A, LA) with medium-to-high contrast.

Dark/Muted
Select dark (A) to slightly toned-down (LA) colour combinations with medium-plus contrast.

Muted/Dark
Select toned-down colour combinations (LA, NA) with soft-to-medium contrast.

Dark/Bright
Select dark to dark-bright (A) colour combinations with high contrast.

Bright/Dark
Select bright and dark colour combinations (A) with strong contrast.

Warm/Dark
Select rich, warm, muted colour combinations (A, NA) with medium contrast.

Warm/Light
Select light (NA) to medium-bright (LA) colour combinations with medium contrast.

Cool/Dark
Select slightly toned-down colour combinations (A, LA) with medium contrast.

Cool/Light
Select soft colour combinations (LA) with medium contrast.

Your Lifestyle Wardrobe

The clothes we choose to wear convey very definite messages. To understand this, and to help you recognize the nonverbal message your style of dress conveys, I have detailed six basic dress styles, and six mixed dress styles. Your personality and lifestyle is generally reflected in a permutation of two, three or even four of these dress styles.

In order to dress yourself correctly you need to understand the sort of person you are and the messages you wish to convey, as well as your preferences and goals. Ask yourself, for example, whether you have achieved the correct level in your chosen profession. If the answer is no, then you should consider dressing for the position you are seeking.

Working through the following questions will help you to pinpoint your fashion needs for your particular lifestyle:

- **What look do you require for your particular profession?**
- **Which look is more comfortable for your home environment?**
- **What is your desired look for the social side of your life?**
- **What casual look do you require – very casual, smart-casual or both?**
- **What sports activities do you pursue, and what different looks do these require?**
- **Do family activities have to be taken into consideration?**
- **Do you require clothes for travelling and for different climates?**

Your lifestyle wardrobe will give you a total package of self-expression. Once understood, your wardrobe will only require slight changes to adapt it to suit a particular occasion, mood or style. In our fast-paced society, our home and work environments never stay static. Fully understanding this enables you to adapt your dress styles to the changes as they occur, and to dress with meaning and portray the correct image.

Study the dress styles on the following pages and try to recognize the non-verbal messages they are sending out. Determine which dress styles you would like to use, and let me help you to adapt a mixed dress style you are happy with for yourself. With a little practice, you will discover the different looks that are most appropriate for your lifestyle, and you will then be in control of the non-verbal messages you are transmitting.

Classic and Elegant Styles

These are conventional, tailored styles. A classic, traditional style focuses on what is expected and/or appropriate. An elegant style has a more feminine, sophisticated lean.

NON-VERBAL MESSAGES	
CLASSIC	ELEGANT
Consistent	Dignified
Conscientious	Gracious
Efficient	Meticulous
Dependable	Polished
Reliable	Restrained
Trustworthy	Serene
	Sophisticated

Feminine and Glamorous Styles

These are very expressive, female styles. The feminine style is non-advancing (the 'little girl lost' look), whereas a glamourous style is advancing (the 'would you like to own me?' look).

NON-VERBAL MESSAGES	
FEMININE	GLAMOROUS
Gentle	Exciting
Gracious	Flirtatious
Romantic	Provocative
Supportive	Seductive
Warm	Suggestive

Dramatic and Creative Styles

These are expressive styles. A dramatic style is very advancing ('I'm on show, I'm important'). A creative style is either advancing or retreating (used to be seen and to grab attention).

NON-VERBAL MESSAGES	
DRAMATIC	CREATIVE
Bold	Adventurous
Confident	Innovative
Intense	Resourceful
Self-assured	Spontaneous
Remote	Unique

How To Create a Style

We have seen how different styles send different messages. Once you have decided on the right styles for you, the following information will show you how to choose colours and outfits to create them.

Classic, Traditional Style

'Classics' are so-called because their cut, styling and detail does not date. A 'classic' suit in a good-quality fabric will look good year after year. Classic looks range from smart through to smart-casual, traditional or conservative with an 'English-structured' shape (a term used in the fashion world, particularly in the United States and Japan, to describe classic styles fashioned in Savile Row, London). Court shoes are appropriate for this look, as is a neat hairstyle.

Tailored jackets or blazers have shoulder padding and a slightly defined waist. Collar, pockets and average-width lapels lie flat. Skirts, kilts and dresses are matching or coordinated with styles varying from slightly tapered to H- or or A-lines. The hemline ends just above the thickest part of the calf, below the knee or slightly shorter when in fashion. Jackets are commonly teamed with traditional patterned skirts with set-in waist bands.

Plain and patterned blouses and one- or two-piece dresses mix and match with other wardrobe pieces that harmonize with the total look. Use natural fabrics such as wool, cotton or silk.

Choose light and dark neutrals and medium colours from your colour wheels mixed in combinations of twos or threes. The contrast level should be in line with that of your personal colouring.

Well-known 'classic' fashion houses and designers who work in this style include:

- **Acquascutum**
- **Alexon**
- **Giorgio Armani**
- **Brooks Brothers**
- **Burberry**
- **Country Casuals**
- **Dunhill**
- **Escada**
- **Giorgio**
- **J.H. Collectibles**
- **Jaeger**
- **Donna Karan**
- **Kenzo**
- **Anne Klein**
- **Calvin Klein**
- **Laurel**
- **Ralph Lauren (for understated classics)**
- **Marks and Spencer**
- **Mulberry**
- **Robert Simon**
- **Jacques Vert**
- **Yarell**

Elegant Style

The softly tailored lines that characterize this refined, feminine, tailored and polished look can be created by selecting beautiful fabrics in best quality cashmere, leather, jersey or stone-washed silk. Shoulder pads can also be used to good effect. Matching designer shoes complement this look, as does an elegant hairstyle.

Use smooth princess lines for simple, chic dresses, and choose jackets and skirts with minimum detail to allow the luxurious fabric to be noticed. Skirts and trousers should be either slightly tapered or straight, and worn with either matching or coordinating jackets teamed with matching plain or Jacquard blouses. Skirt lengths generally have a fashionable lean.

Choose neutral colours and the least-advancing colours of your wheels. Mono colours are also appropriate for this look.

Well-known 'elegant' fashion houses and designers include:

- **Chanel**
- **Oscar de la Renta**
- **Christian Dior**
- **Louis Feraud**
- **Givenchy**
- **Krizia**
- **Christian Lacroix**
- **Nina Ricci**
- **Yves Saint Laurent**
- **Jean-Louis Scherrer**
- **Valentino**

Glamorous Style

Jackets, coats and skirts all have a curved look about them. Fabrics are lightweight in natural and blended fibres. They are alluring, sensuous and sexy – shiny, clingy, stretchy or glittery – and cling, drape or smooth round the body's contours and define the waist. Skirts taper to the hemline. Choose fitted dresses, tops and jumpsuits for special occasions or evening wear. Shoes can be court, slingbacks or dressy sandals. Hairstyles should be lavish, with waves, curls or layering to create fullness.

Use the advancing colours of your wheels. These are the most daring and vibrant and are best worn in monotone or two-tone combinations with colour effectively emphasizing body shape. For your make-up, you should also use the brightest colours from your wheel.

Well-known 'glamorous' fashion houses and designers include:

- **Oscar de la Renta**
- **Donna Karan**
- **Karl Lagerfeld**
- **Jean Muir**
- **Albert Nipon**
- **J. Tiktiner**
- **Emanuel Ungaro**

Feminine Style

Choose soft, gentle, romantic and delicate colour and fabric combinations in flowing, even, rounded lines. Jersey, lace, silk, appliqué and ruffles all bring something to this look. If you prefer you can adapt the classic style (see pages 55-6) to make it a more feminine simply by using softer lines and colours for accessories.

Gathers on sleeves and yokes can be used to add fullness or to conceal. Patterns should be medium to fine in detail and evenly spaced, which implies a delicate or feminine look. Soft, broken horizontal lines can be created by wearing drop-waisted, or slightly waisted gathered skirts. High-waisted 'empire' dresses and loose-fitting bodices (blousons) can also be used to achieve this effect. Flowing skirts should be mid-calf length, and in a soft fabric. Shoes should be in soft leather or suede, and court shoes should have a bow or other decoration. Good shoe styles for this look include T-bar, open-toed and slingbacks. Hairstyles should be soft, and frame the face.

Use the lightest neutrals and pastel, powdery colours from your wheels in mono or closely related colours. Two tones should be light to medium in intensity with no marked contrasts. Make-up colours should also be soft.

Well-known 'feminine' fashion houses and designers include:

*   **Laura Ashley**
*   **Bill Blass**
*   **Cachet**
*   **Oscar de la Renta**
*   **Emanuel**
*   **Diane Freis**
*   **Albert Nipon**
*   **Tom and Linda Platt**
*   **Gloria Sachs**
*   **Ungaro**

Dramatic Style

Use shoulder pads and sleek, asymmetrical structures in exaggerated dramatic styles, with little or no detail. Abstract, overscale and geometric blouses can be worn with a solid-coloured suit. Bold accessories match and pick up on the exaggerated style and colour. Wear exaggerated make-up colours. Choose shoes that are designed with extremes, such as very high or low heels, and dramatic, contrasting patterns and colour combinations. Hairstyles should be sleek, and either very short or very long.

Use contrasting colours from your wheels. Combine bright colours with the light or dark neutral colours, or wear very light and very dark intensity colours together, providing your own level of contrast can stand it.

Well-known 'dramatic' fashion houses and designers include:

*   **Bill Blass**
*   **Perry Ellis**
*   **Escada**
*   **Thierry Mugler**

Creative Style

Create looks which are off-beat, arty, individual, non-conforming and unexpected. You could, for example, wear layered looks such as white, lacey knickers over black leggings and boots; lycra cycle shorts or ski-pants under micro-mini skirts with a lacey, embroidered top; a classic jacket over a lacey top and a clingy, jersey skirt or a drapey or foulard patterned skirt. Select stoles, blouses, T-shirts and vests in a mixture of unusual colours, patterns (medium to fine detail), fabric textures and weights (lace worn with wool).

Interesting accessories are essential for this look. Choose decorative belts, handkerchiefs, jewellery and scarves, from neon to ethnic in character. As for make-up, wear lots or none at all.

Use mixes of colour in unconventional combinations. Dark, muted colours and neutrals create the best effects. You could even wear all black as if in hiding.

Well known 'creative' fashion houses and designers include:

- **Jennifer George**
- **Donna Karan**
- **Issey Miyake**

Different Classic Styles

Classic Smart-casual Style

This is a relaxed version of the classic, traditional style. An inspired and witty look, it combines structured, conventional styles and elegant, refined and luxurious fabrics. Most of the classic styles can be given a smart casual look. A traditional, structured blazer will still be classic, but less formal, if it is made from softer, hanging fabrics such as cashmere, and

worn with designer jeans. Matching designer separates and accessories all add to this look.

Well-known 'classic smart-casual' fashion houses and designers include:

- **Giorgio Armani**
- **Betty Barclay**
- **Hugo Boss**
- **Brooks Brothers**
- **Dunhill**
- **Escada**
- **Ginocchietti**
- **Richard James**
- **Donna Karan**
- **Calvin Klein**
- **Laurel**
- **Ralph Lauren**
- **Issey Miyake**
- **Mulberry**
- **Shirin**
- **Umberto**
- **Vincci**
- **Yarell**

Classic Elegant Style

As the name suggests, this style is less masculine-looking than the classic style. The jackets are still structured but with a slightly softer line and made from luxurious fabric with a feminine tailored look.

RIGHT: A subtly softer line creates the classic elegant look.

FAR RIGHT: The classic feminine look is noticeably softer than the classic look – in colour, fabric and design.

Classic Feminine Style

To make your classic style appear more feminine, wear the softer colour combinations suggested in your wheels. Shoulder pads should have a slightly softer lean to them. Short or cap sleeves would also give a feminine lean. Feminine

touches can be added by a tie or bow at the neckline, and a little lace or velvet. Choose fabric that is soft or light to the touch, or has some movement in it.

Select plain and delicately patterned designs for dresses, blouses and scarves. Short, even collarless jackets all bring feminine softness to this look. Wear your hair in a softer, more feminine style with ornaments or combs. Your make-up should be in a lighter, more delicate shade. Wear a scarf, shawl or wrap over your jacket, plus gloves and jewellery which looks feminine.

Choose sumptuous
fabrics, such as silk and
satin, for a classic
glamorous look.

Classic Glamorous Style

There are a number of ways in which you can make the classic style more glamorous. Choose a dress or suit which drapes or fits your figure well and has a special touch of quality, style, design or fabric. Try a simple fit-and-flare coat-dress, or add a satin collar to a dress with a halter neck.

Wear suits buttoned up without a blouse or top. Try silk camisoles worn under see-through blouses or jackets that sparkle. Wear an evening version of day-time separates in silk and more glamorous fabrics. Add a stole in place of a jacket.

Change your usual court shoes for more feminine sandals. Wear pearls mixed with a gold or silver chain and brooches and earrings that sparkle. Follow the make-up tips for a glamorous look and add your most exotic fragrance. Wear your hair up or add a hairpiece, combs or bands.

RIGHT: A slightly daring edge gives the classic look a dramatic touch.

FAR RIGHT: A hint of individuality can create the classic creative look.

Classic Dramatic Style

Any classic suit or dress can be made to look more dramatic by cleverly coordinating its colour and style with that of other garments. A black-and-white, structured hat and white gloves will, for example, make a black, classic suit look more dramatic. And large, geometric jewellery shapes and a severe hairstyle will give a plain, classic dress a dramatic lean.

Classic Creative Style

This style is the result of adding a touch of creative flair to the classic traditional style, and brings some logical order to a creative look. For example, wear a draped skirt with a structured jacket. You could also use a pocket handkerchief to bring a three-colour look together. Wear a long-sleeved T-shirt under a classic waistcoat and pants.

The classic casual look is ideal for those who want to look smart, but not too formal.

Classic Casual Style

Change your classic blouses for T-shirts, and wear them loose or with a soft knot at the waist to give a more nonchalant look (providing your waist can stand it). Add T-shirts and tops to your suits, skirts and trousers. Make trousers more dressy with an imitation silk or pure silk blouse.

Discover which manufacturer's blouses will look good with another manufacturer's jackets or suits. Replace jackets with waistcoats or cardigans for a softer look. Wear your jackets with jeans or trousers, pleated skirts or culottes.

An imitation silk T-shirt in an appropriate colour worn with low-heeled shoes can turn a smart suit into a semi-casual smart look. Wear flatter, more casual-looking leather shoes, a leather belt and swap your clutch bag for a leather tote. Wear gloves in fabric, wool or leather and simple, good quality jewellery. Follow make-up tips for a natural look.

Creating Visual Balance

A successful visual effect is achieved by a unified look. A garment or ensemble which has too many points of interest, or too many details competing for attention does not have visual balance. Here are a few guidelines to help you create visual harmony.

Your main pieces of clothing such as jackets, skirts and coats should be chosen because they combine well in colour and style. You should give some thought to your blouses or sweaters which will create a variety of looks appropriate to your particular lifestyle.

Before going shopping or even sorting out your existing wardrobe, study your figure shape and select the best designers of jackets, skirts, blouses etc. for your particular figure which can be worn successfully after camouflage (shoulder pads). Here are a few examples to help you become more aware.

Jackets
- **A double-breasted jacket with a skirt that has a centre detail, such as centre buttons or pleats, does not look harmonious.**
- **A single-breasted jacket with buttons in line with the skirt buttons looks right, provided that the buttons on your jacket do not fight with the ones on your skirt.**
- **For an all-round suit jacket for the average height of 5' 4" (1.63 m) or under, select a single-breasted jacket which goes well with most styles of skirt and can be worn with trousers.**

Blouses and Tops
These offer the best flexibility as they can finish off an outfit by pulling together unmatched jackets and skirts, making them look fashionable and new.

Choosing a selection of blouses and tops in solid colours and in patterned fabrics such as prints and stripes can give you unlimited looks. Long sleeves are the most dressy and create a more professional look. All blouses look and hang better with some form of shoulder pads, unless you have an angular figure shape.

You must consider the colour of your jacket and skirt which need to be pulled together by your blouse or top. For example, a 70/30 per cent colour split could be allocated as follows – 70 per cent for shoes, tights, suit, belt and accessories, with 30 per cent for the blouse or top.

On plain blouses, buttons that show can be an accessory in colour and design. Always bring a little colour of your unmatched skirt up to the top half of your body with buttons and blouse patterns, jewellery, a scarf or a pocket handkerchief.

Combining Two Collar Styles

When choosing necklines for blouses or tops you must bear in mind your face shape and neck length. You must also consider the necklines with which the blouse or top is going to be worn. A blouse with a Peter Pan collar, for instance, will look wrong with a jacket with a wing collar. There is no relationship between these two styles as the blouse collar is curved and the jacket has very straight pointed lapels. The curved lines of the blouse make it appear softer, whilst the jacket lapels look severe, so there is no semblance of harmony.

Planning Your Wardrobe

It takes time to personalize your wardrobe to suit your individual lifestyle needs. Once achieved, however, it is rewarding in so many ways. So whether you are at a time in your life when you are starting afresh, or whether you are having to take one step at a time, it makes very little difference. What is important is that you are making a commitment to sort out your wardrobe which will affect a big part of your life.

Unless you are starting a completely new lifestyle pattern, the events listed in your diary for last year will give you most of the information you require to start planning your wardrobe. With pen and paper, go through your diary and write down at the side of each event the style of dress that you would like to have worn on that occasion. Now add up how many times you required that style of dress during the year. Next, draw up a detailed plan of the clothing items you require to cover your lifestyle. From this you will discover what your wardrobe holds and what needs to be added. You can then prioritize your needs, which is a great help when it comes to budgeting.

With this information to hand, empty the contents of your wardrobe onto the bed. Place jackets on one pile, skirts on another, and so on. Hang back into your wardrobe only the clothes you have listed which create your lifestyle looks and are in good condition, marking off your wardrobe clothes planner as you go.

Persuade some of your friends to follow your lead, then you can swop or sell any good clothes you did not hang back. Remember, just because they are not suitable for your lifestyle does not mean they will not be a great find for someone else's.

When you go shopping, buy only garments which are on your list, and which will work with at least two other garments hanging in your wardrobe. Follow the same guidelines for your accessories.

Mix-and-Match Wardrobe

It could be that you would like all or part of your wardrobe to mix and match. This is a great way to make 12 items of clothing give you over 40 different looks. This serves ideally as a budget wardrobe or for travelling.

Make a list of 12 clothing items you possess which combine well in colour and style and which make appropriate lifestyle looks. To help you do this, split up your suits and hang all your jackets, skirts, blouses, sweaters and dresses together. Make a similar list of your accessories.

Another way of discovering what clothes you need to cover your lifestyle is to draw a matrix like the one shown on page 68 on a large piece of paper. Hang or stick this behind your wardrobe door. Mark the appropriate square each time you wear a particular clothing combination. You will soon discover the clothes you are getting the most use out of. This will help you to decide what new clothing you should invest in for the future.

Creating a Fashionable Look

If you want to create a fashionable look, start to become more aware of the fashion trends in colour and line design. Being fashionable does not mean having a new wardrobe every six months. It could mean, however, mixing your colours a little differently, raising or lowering your skirt lengths and wearing slightly softer or straighter shoulder pads.

Read magazines, look at the merchandise in department stores and see how they are mixing and matching colours and styles on their displays. Then look at your existing wardrobe and ask yourself what colour or slight adjustment to shape do you have to make this season to make your wardrobe look fashionable and new.

For example, investing in a new purple handkerchief and gloves is maybe all that is required to make last year's wardrobe look revitalized and fashionable. This is what I did when I was invited to attend a press launch on the latest fashion colours in a large London department store one season. Wearing purple with red was the big fashion news for the season. My wardrobe held a red suit I had worn for four years. The style and fabric of my suit were perfect, but I did not have a purple blouse or top. So I buttoned up the jacket and fixed a purple handkerchief at the neck making it look like a blouse, and teamed it with purple gloves. I received so many compliments that day that this outfit became my favourite look for that season.

It is all a matter of personal style. This is something that is uniquely yours whether good, bad or indifferent. Your lifestyle look sends out messages of mood, confidence and insight into your inner self, created by colour, style lines, fabric, texture, weight, pattern and accessories.

By now you will understand how to put the tangible aspects of dress together to create different lifestyle looks and moods. You are learning how to stage-manage, manipulate, adjust and accommodate to different situations. Once sorted, your wardrobe will be prepared for any event or activity. You will be able to add your own personality with ease and confidence and discover your own unique style.

	Dress L	Sweater K	Sweater J	Blouse I	Blouse H	Blouse G	Blouse F	Skirt E	Skirt D	Skirt C
Jacket A										
Jacket B										
Skirt C										
Skirt D										
Skirt E										
Blouse F										
Blouse G										
Blouse H										
Blouse I										
Sweater J										
Sweater K										
Dress L										

Draw up a matrix like this one, and tick the relevant box every time you wear an item of clothing.

Chapter 5

CHOOSING FABRICS AND ACCESSORIES

By this stage, you should be confident about putting together an outfit in the best styles and colours for you. Colour is also an important consideration when it comes to selecting fabrics and accessories, which can often add the finishing touch to a look. This chapter looks at how you can make fabric and accessories work best for you.

Fabric

Fabric contributes more to style than most people realize, and must always be considered when putting a look together. The fabric not only dictates the shape, line and character of the garment, but also the image you want to project. All too often, fabrics are not suitable for the garment style for which they are used.

The term 'texture' refers to the woven arrangement of yarns or fibres and to their weave. Fibres today are woven into fabrics with many different textures. They span from being tightly and closely woven to very open and loose. Technological advances mean there are even newer fabrics to thrill and excite us, but even traditional, natural fibres can be versatile. One of my favourites, wool, comes in a variety of weights and textures which handle in very different ways. It can, for example, be made to drape and move with the body, as in wool crepe, or to be more tightly woven, as in some gaberdines.

Fabric texture and weight can assist in creating many different styles and looks in your dress. When choosing fabric, you should determine the type of clothes it can be made into. You should consider the 'hand' of a fabric – the way it feels, falls and drapes. A fabric that drapes well, falls softly and smoothly and moves fluidly can be an asset worn on a figure type which also has some of these attributes. Conversely, a fabric which is stiff and lacks movement causes problems for a figure to which it bears no resemblance.

Texture is seen as well as felt. For example, a lustrous fabric with a smooth surface, such as taffeta, reflects more light than a matt surface. Rough textures, on the other hand, absorb light. Shiny textures maximize size, whereas matt textures minimize it. Soft, pile fabrics, such as velvet, velour, terry cloth, chenille and corduroy make a person seem larger. A rough-textured fabric which is stiff and crisp increases in size by adding bulk as there is no movement. Fabrics which cling to your body emphasize your contours and restrict your movement.

The size of the pattern should be compatible with the garment into which it is being made, as well as the size and personal colouring of the wearer. If you are after a dramatic look, a large print on stiff fabric creates this. The same large print on a softer fabric such as see-through chiffon does not have the same impact.

Finding the Right Fabric for You

Your personal colouring provides the 'background' for the colours you wear, and influences how they look. Visualizing colour on a black background generates a much stronger image than the same colours on a white background. A petite person with light colouring could easily be overpowered by a medium-to-large, boldly coloured print on a dark background. On the other hand, a petite woman with dark colouring could make it work.

By being aware of your colouring, you will be able to choose fabric textures, weights and patterns, as well as jewellery, that harmonize with you. If you match these up with the dress patterns appropriate for your body shape (see Chapter 3), you will be able to discover the looks, styles and moods towards which you naturally lean, and the ones you will have to work a little harder to achieve. The following guidelines will help:

MUTED COLOURING

Your look is enhanced by using fabric in which the *texture* is prominent. This is because the melanin in your colouring gives a subtle, textured quality to it. Repeating this effect in your clothing creates a sense of harmony. Combining textures works well. A light/muted person takes medium-to-light textures best.

The contrast level of the print selected is the most vital aspect, as you can wear from small to large patterns. The small patterns and prints must be no more than medium in contrast. The darker and stronger your colouring, the larger the pattern you can take.

BRIGHT COLOURING

As a bright person, you reflect light, so you harmonize best with fabrics and textures which also reflect light, and thus have a smooth look and feel. Keep light-absorbing textured finishes to a minimum in your wardrobe.

You should wear patterns and prints of medium to high contrast to look your best. Very small prints are best for those of you who also have 'light' in your personal-colouring description. Tiny prints should be worn only by those whose colouring falls in the light/cool and light/muted areas. On everyone else they look uninspiring.

Using Fabric to Create Looks and Moods

CLASSIC, TRADITIONAL, STRUCTURED LOOKS
Fabrics suitable for these looks include the following:

- **broadcloth**
- **corduroy**
- **cottons**
- **flannel**
- **gabardine**
- **heavy knits**
- **linen blends**
- **Oxford**
- **raw silk**
- **serge**
- **tweeds**
- **twill**
- **worsteds**

Close-woven or very slightly textured, natural fibres with matt finishes, such as foulard, are considered traditional when added to a pattern with an all-over design. Such patterns include small-scale checks, herringbone, houndstooth, tartans, paisley, pin and polka-dot, and stripes in mix-and-match combinations of one, two or three colours.

CLASSIC, TRADITIONAL, SPORTY LOOKS
Natural, comfortable fabrics are required here, such as:

- **canvas (medium to heavy weight)**
- **challis**
- **chambray**
- **corduroy**
- **cotton**
- **denim**
- **linen**
- **Oxford**
- **tweeds**
- **Viyella wool flannel**

Suitable patterns are traditional all-over designs, such as small- to medium-scale prints, checks and tartans.

ELEGANT, SLIGHTLY STRUCTURED LOOKS
Use fabrics made from natural fibres that look and feel smooth and luxurious, such as:

- **high-quality cashmere (light to medium weight)**
- **challis**
- **crepe silk**
- **linen blends**
- **pima cotton**
- **wool gabardine**

Elegant patterns are worn only in subtle colours in monochromatic or analogous blends with a little contrast. An elegant dress colour takes a back place, allowing the luxurious fabric to take centre stage.

DRAMATIC, STRUCTURED LOOKS
Closely woven, firm, smooth fabrics that hold their shape are needed here, such as black gaberdine contrasted against white

mercerized cotton. Dramatic patterns are abstracts, geometrics and prints with strong contrasting colour combinations.

GLAMOROUS, NON-STRUCTURED LOOKS
Smooth, clingy and stretchable fabrics, as well as those that can be draped, create this look. You can use lightweight fibres in naturals and blends such as:

- **angora**
- **jersey**
- **lamé**
- **leather**
- **rayon silk**
- **suede**

Glamorous patterns are mostly solids in bright or dark, vibrant, advancing colours, or designs which have movement, such as animal prints.

FEMININE, NATURAL LOOKS
Soft, lightweight, sheer and flowing fabrics are required here. Use natural and synthetic blends which are smooth, light and feminine in texture, such as:

- **angora**
- **bouclé**
- **challis**
- **chambray**
- **chiffon**
- **cotton**
- **crepe**
- **lace**
- **fine linen**
- **organdie**
- **silk**

Feminine patterns are small-to-medium florals evenly spaced on a pastel background; light and neutral colours on a monochromatic background; or mixes of a few non-advancing colours.

CREATIVE, STRUCTURED OR UNSTRUCTURED LOOKS
Here, anything goes. You can use opposing fabrics – hard/soft, firm/fluid, fine/coarsely textured, matt/shiny, natural/synthetic. Creative patterns include mismatch, paisley and mixed designs of unrelated scale in ethnic and unusual colour combinations with medium to dark intensities.

Accessories

Accessories can make or break a look. A safe rule is to consider what effect the addition will have on the outfit. Do the additions change the mood of the look – as in wearing ethnic jewellery with a classic business outfit, for example? Balance must be created between jewellery and other accessories: the more accessories, the less jewellery, and vice versa.

Belts

For women with a waist and hipline that can stand up to scrutiny, belts are a good accessory, adding drama and character. There are a few rules to remember:

1) **A belt should never be so wide or tight that it pulls in the flesh, causing a bulge above and below.**
2) **The shorter the skirt, the narrower the belt, and vice versa.**
3) **If you want to wear a belt but do not want to draw attention to your waist, wear it loose with an unbuttoned jacket or cardigan, allowing just a small part of the belt either side of the buckle to be seen.**

Hats

When choosing a hat, always use a full-length mirror to establish the best visual balance for your height and width. If you want to look taller, wear a hat which has a crown or decoration in the same colour as your outfit (make sure that the brim is not so wide that it covers the colour). A slightly raised crown will also give you height. Alternatively, a hat which is dark in colour and contrasts with your outfit can make you look shorter, and the same goes for a turban hat which fits closely to your head.

How you wear a hat also affects your height. Worn horizontally, a hat shortens; worn straight or tilted, it lifts the eye. You must also consider the fabric and texture of the garments you are wearing with your hat and the mood you are endeavouring to create.

Handbags

Your lifestyle will generally dictate how many and what types of handbags you require. Before adding a handbag, briefcase or holdall to your look, ask yourself what look you are trying to achieve? Will the colour, design features and fabric harmonize with the rest of your look, or do you require contrasting, dramatic details or way-out, off-beat ones?

Scarves

Scarves (and pocket handkerchiefs) can be used to:
* **Focus the eye on a particular part of the body.**
* **Bring together or harmonize an outfit by using its line and colour.**
* **Give a favourite old garment a more fashionable look.**
* **Lift, tone or change the look of a garment colour.**

When choosing a scarf you should take into consideration your lifestyle, personal colouring and body shape. Ask yourself what look you want to achieve, and

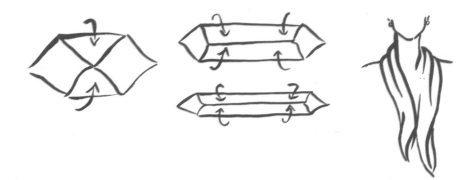

ABOVE: To fold a
square into a rectangle
or bias shape, lay a
square-shaped scarf in
front of you with one
of the corners pointing
towards you. Pick this
corner up and place it
in the centre of the
square. Do the same
with the corner facing
away from you. Fold
the horizontal edges to
the centre again. Carry
on in the same way
until you reach the
width you require.

BELOW: When folded as
shown here, your scarf
can be turned into an
interesting belt.

choose a scarf shape that will complement the outfit with which it is worn. There are three basic scarf shapes:

1) **Bias. Cut diagonally across the grain of the cloth in a rectangular shape with diagonal ends.**
2) **Rectangle. Comes in many different lengths and designs. It is often used for ornamentation or to accentuate an area rather than for warmth (a wool scarf is an exception). The smaller sizes are the most versatile as they can be used in so many ways.**
3) **Square. Comes in a variety of sizes, and is not always quite square. It is usually worn for warmth as well as adding to the look.**

HOW TO TIE SCARVES

There is no substitute for practising how to tie scarves. Learn two or three ways with different shapes and sizes first. Once you have mastered these, then experiment further. Start looking in magazines for examples of how scarves blend into your figure shape.

Pocket Handkerchiefs

Pocket handkerchiefs can be worn at the neckline, breast pocket, through a brooch or added to a sleeve cuff. Like a scarf, a pocket handkerchief can help to bring separate garments together. For example, when wearing a grey dress with a red jacket, combine a grey and red handkerchief

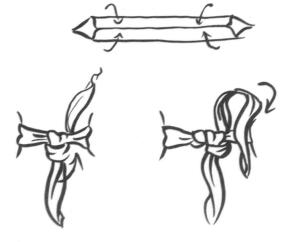

RIGHT: When wearing a long scarf loosely around the neck, knot it at the ends to provide weight.

FAR RIGHT: Tying your scarf in a deep 'V' can make your neck and face look longer.

Your hair can play a big part in making your neck and face look longer or shorter. The illustration on the left shows short hair worn with a high-necked scarf and a jacket with a deep V-neck. This creates a much longer look than in the illustration in the middle, in which the model has long hair. The same effect is shown on the right, but this time with short hair.

so that they appear as one to finish off the look. When wearing a teal-blue suit with an icy-blue blouse, the handkerchief should be multicoloured with teal and a light blue being the predominant colours. Alternatively, put one plain teal and one light blue handkerchief together and integrate them into the look.

Accessory Guidelines for Different Looks

When it comes to putting together a particular look, the accessories are as important as the clothes themselves. Follow these guidelines to help you create a coordinated overall image:

Classic Traditional Look

JEWELLERY
Subtle, moderate in size and of good quality. No dangly earrings or clanging bracelets. Minimal amounts of gold, silver or pearl necklaces, earrings and pins.

SHOES
Flats for casual, and two-inch heels in pumps or loafers. Leather is the preferred material for this very traditional, dressy look.

HANDBAGS
Leather, medium in size, structured and traditional in style.

BELTS
Classic in design, medium in size to match or tone with shoes.

Classic Sporty Look

JEWELLERY
Simple, lightweight and comfortable. Gold, silver or pearl ear studs and necklaces.

SHOES AND BOOTS
Flat to two-inch heel and wedges in leather canvas, straw or suede.

HANDBAGS
Leather, canvas, straw, linen or suede. Shoulder bag, saddlebag or tote bag.

BELTS
Medium in size, classic or sporty in design and in natural materials such as leather or canvas. Use a mix of both stable and top stitching.

Elegant Look

JEWELLERY
As for traditional, with the addition of fine quality longer lengths in pearls and gold chains, worn together with medium pins and earrings.

SHOES
Designer flats to medium high heels. Solid colours or two-tone made to match other designer garments and accessories.

HANDBAGS
Medium in size in designer styles and status fabric.

BELTS
Narrow to medium widths with satin-finished or luxuriously covered buckles.

Dramatic Look

JEWELLERY
In gold, silver and high-fashion multiple textures, in abstracts, art deco and avant garde. Wear one striking earring with a small pin earring in the other ear.

SHOES
Striking, two-tone, angular and extreme in high heels, slingbacks, platform soles and flats.

HANDBAGS
Noticeable and extreme in size and contrast. Structured and geometric in shape.

BELTS
Eye-catching designs and fabrics. Buckles should be elaborate, perhaps with geometric designs, and should coordinate with handbag, shoes or both.

Glamorous Look

JEWELLERY
Minimal amount, moderate in size so as not to distract from your body line. Shiny gold and silver, diamonds, rhinestones and other gems.

SHOES
High heels and flats in plain pumps; slingbacks and straps.

HANDBAGS
Small to medium in size with curvy contours in soft, supple materials.

BELTS
Small to medium in size in wrap, cummerbund and elastic cinch. These belts put the waist on show with soft, supple fabrics in leather, satin, silk, suede and velvet.

Feminine Look

JEWELLERY
A feminine, romantic look has no fashion jewellery, just matt, soft finishes in gold, silver and pearl in small to medium sizes. Delicate, intricate styling with curvy movement in antique detail, graduated pearls, cameo, locket and charm bracelet.

SHOES
Flat or two-inch heels with buckles, bows, open toe and slingback. Delicate in design and fabrics.

HANDBAGS
Unstructured with movement in design. Soft, small, leather clutch, paisley or floral holdall.

BELTS
Soft and supple leather ties and sashes or bow designs to match handbag or dress theme.

Creative Look

JEWELLERY
A mix of styles. Unusual, natural to synthetic materials. Leather choker with crystal drop beads, stacked or cuffed bracelets, fruits and designs from nature.

SHOES
Flat or two-inch heel, patterned, meshed, antique heels, lace-up boots in all weathers.

HANDBAGS
Ethnic, nature backpack, overnight rucksack and belt bag.

BELTS
Anything unusual using more than one style worn together. Wear at the waist or below. Antique, ethnic, outdated coins on chains or leather, even milk-bottle tops.

Accessories and Colouring

Like your clothes, your accessories will work much harder for you if they complement your personal colouring. Follow these guidelines for good results.

Muted Colouring

JEWELLERY
The subtle texture of your skin and mixes in your eye colour are enhanced with handcrafted, ethnic, textured contemporary and antique jewellery. Use any piece of jewellery which generally incorporates texture as a predominant element of its design. Both smooth and textured metals are fine providing there are no large areas that shine. The same goes for stones and costume jewellery. Stay clear of the overly bright, clear looks. The toned-down brights on your colour wheels are the best colours to aim for.

Use metals that have been brushed, oxidized, antiqued or etched. Medium- to large-sized pieces are best. Dull gold, slightly tarnished or textured silver, pewter, copper, bronze and brass are suitable. Combining gold and silver also works well.

Muted/light types can get away with wearing tiny, more delicate-looking pieces which you would normally associate with being very feminine. A person who is muted/dark or dark/muted can wear larger pieces of the above jewellery very effectively.

Light/cool or light/muted types should select small-to-medium accessories or larger pieces which are light in colour and in weight. Do not overdo your jewellery. Use soft-tone gold, white or rose, slightly tarnished copper, silver and pewter, mixes of gold and silver, textured and smooth. For gems and semi-precious stones select colours from your colour wheels.

HANDBAGS AND HOLDALLS
In addition to non-shiny leather, any material that gives a textured look is flattering, providing it is appropriate for your outfit and related in some way to your shoes.

Bright Colouring

The clear colours of your eyes and the reflected light from your skin makes the bright/light, bright/dark, dark/bright and cool/dark types look best wearing medium-sized jewellery. When bright and dark come together, heavier pieces can be worn. A dark/bright person is able to wear the largest and most dramatic pieces. Smooth-textured gold, shiny silver, white-gold platinum, brass and bronze are the best, but textured metals with a shine will also work. For gems, semi-precious stones and costume jewellery select colours from your colour wheels.

HANDBAGS AND HOLDALLS
Use medium-smooth, shiny and patent leather in neutral and bright colours to match your outfits.

Chapter 6

COLOUR AND MAKE-UP

Using make-up can help enhance your individual beauty. Now that you have analysed your colouring and discovered your colour wheel, you can use make-up to bring your look to life. This chapter looks at basic make-up techniques, and shows you how you can use cosmetics to flatter your particular facial shape and features.

Do not be satisfied with the way you have been wearing your make-up for years unless you know that it does the most for you. I believe that your best make-up look is one that is a natural extension of your personal colouring. Learning about using colour in make-up is a step-by-step process, and it is best to begin by wearing less make-up than you would ultimately like. As you become more experienced you can add more, especially for a glamorous look.

The colour wheels are designed to give you a valuable guide to the colours that will look good for cosmetics as well as clothes and accessories. A classic, traditional look can be achieved by wearing the medium-intensity colours of your wheel to create a refined, understated style appropriate for any occasion. A glamorous look can be achieved by using the more vibrant, bold colours from your wheel.

Fashion in make-up is as changeable as fashion in clothes. A 'natural' look might be popular one season; a more 'dramatic' look the next. Reading fashion and beauty magazines will keep you up to date with make-up trends, as will keeping an eye on what is available at cosmetic counters. Basic make-up techniques, however, do not change.

Finding Your Face Shape

To find out how you can use colour in make-up to look your best, you need to be aware of your face shape. My analysis and practical making-up of countless faces in Britain, the United States and many other countries has brought to light the fact that there are eight basic face shapes: oval, round, square, pear, oblong, rectangular, diamond and heart. If you do not fall exactly into one face shape, you will lean more towards one than another.

The eight basic face shapes are illustrated (opposite). Try to determine your shape by looking intently at your face in a mirror and then comparing what you see with each of the illustrations. If this does not work, then use the following technique. Fasten your hair back and hold

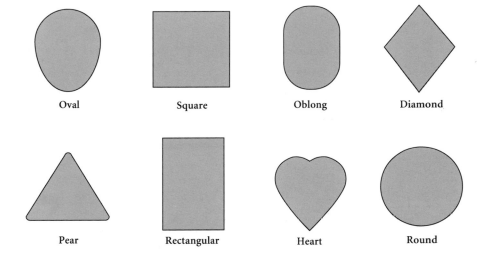

Oval   Square   Oblong   Diamond

Pear   Rectangular   Heart   Round

The eight basic face shapes.

two sticks vertically from the hair line, in line with the outer corners of your eyes, down to the jaw. The amount of face you see outside the two vertical lines will help you to discover your face shape:

- **Oval face – the widest area will be around the eyes and ears, with gradual curves inwards towards the forehead and jawline.**
- **Pear face – your face will be close to the vertical lines at your forehead, and wider than the lines at your ears and jaw line.**
- **Square face – there is the same amount of your face outside the vertical sticks, all the way down the jaw line.**
- **Rectangular or oblong face – there is very little of your face outside the two vertical sticks, with virtually the same width top, middle and bottom.**
- **Heart face – a great deal of your forehead is visible outside the two vertical sticks, a little less at the ear area and very little, if any, at the jawline.**
- **Diamond face – there is very little face visible outside the two vertical sticks, and this will be close to the ear area, tapering sharply towards a narrow forehead and chin area, which will be almost equal in width.**
- **Round face – the widest points which overlap the vertical sticks will be around the ear area, with a gradual curving up to the forehead and down to the jawline, creating an almost round shape.**

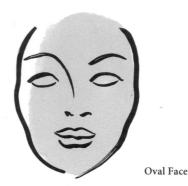

Oval Face

Creative Make-up

Few of us have a perfect 'oval' face shape and regular features. Clever use of pale and dark foundations can, however, 'reshape' the face. This is known as creative make-up.

Dark shading reduces the amount of light that is reflected, and can help disguise areas of the face. Lighter foundation picks up light, thereby highlighting the areas upon which it is applied. The darker and lighter shades are generally referred to as 'shadow' and 'highlighter' respectively. For more information on using foundation, see page 84.

This section looks first at how make-up should be applied to various face shapes, and then at how individual facial features can be 'corrected'.

Oval Face

The oval face shape is classified as nature's most perfect face shape. To recognize this shape, visualize an egg which is wider at the top and tapers down to a softly rounded bottom.

Using a slightly damp sponge or your finger tips, lightly cover your entire face with a thin coating of foundation to smoothe out and cover any minor blemishes. If you have dark circles under your eyes, cover them with a lighter foundation using a fine brush. Blot any excess

Pear-shaped Face

foundation with a tissue or brush it away lightly with your fingers.

Eyeshadow is applied to enhance eye shape. Your eyebrows should be kept natural looking with a soft arch. Your lipline should be generous, but not too full.

Pear-shaped Face

A person with a pear-shaped face has a narrow forehead in comparison to a wide jawline. Many mature women have this face shape due to relaxed jowls. For hints on creative make-up see illustration above.

Every eye make-up technique available should be used to centre attention on your eyes. When shaping your eyebrows, keep them slightly further apart than usual. Create a wide, graceful lip line which should be slightly toned down allowing your eyes to advance.

As the objective of all creative make-up is to produce an oval illusion, the *oval-shaped* face fortunately needs no creative make-up for its contour.

The *pear-shaped* face can be widened at the forehead and slimmed down at the jawline by creative means. Apply your darkest foundation to the widest part of your jawline. Use an opaque highlighter on your forehead, blending it into a bow shape with the edges of the bow extending down the side of your temples.

Square Face

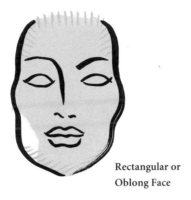

Rectangular or
Oblong Face

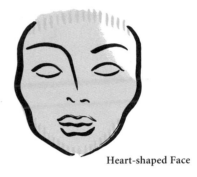

Heart-shaped Face

The *rectangular or oblong* face can be given the illusion of an oval by widening the forehead and narrowing the jawline. Apply opaque highlighter across the top of your forehead, close to your hairline. Next, apply the highlighter to the sides of your temples commencing just above your cheekbone and continuing up to your hairline on the side of your forehead. Finally, use your fingers to blend the highlighter by stroking towards the hairline.

Reduce the width of the forehead on a *heart-shaped* face by applying contour shadow over your forehead in the shape of a bow, blending it down the side of your temples and into your hairline. Highlighter should also be applied downwards from your ear lobes along your entire jawline. If your chin is pointed or protruding, stop the highlighter short of your chin, and bring it right across and under your bottom lip.

The same principles apply for the jaw area of the *square face* as for the pear-shaped face. What differs is the application of highlighter to the top half of the face. This must be applied in the centre of your forehead with the broadest part at your hair line, narrowing to the shape of a 'V' as it comes closer to your eyebrows.

Square Face

The square face appears almost box-like as the forehead and jawline are of practically equal width. For hints on creative make-up see illustration (above). Your eyebrows should be extended slightly and kept rather full, and can be slightly rounded. Your lip line should be wide and slightly curved.

Rectangular or Oblong Face

The rectangular face shape can be broad or narrow. Its main feature is length, and it is always longer in comparison to its width, with the forehead being the same width all the way down to the jaw area. For hints on creative make-up see illustration (above).

Keep eyebrows angular and short to minimize a narrow forehead. Your lips should be softly curved and lipstick should finish slightly short of the edge of your mouth.

Heart-shaped Face

The heart-shaped face is generally on the short side, and the forehead is always very broad in comparison to the jawline. The objective is to make your forehead appear less wide. Narrowing the forehead will automatically make the face look longer. Hairstyles can camouflage the width to a certain degree, but this effect can be limited because of the shortness of the face. For hints on creative make-up see illustration (above).

Your eyebrows should not be short or angular. Create a soft, graceful, almost curved line which is somewhat extended. The upper lip line should be slightly curved, with the lower lip line kept straight if possible.

Diamond-shaped Face

Round Face

To add width to thinner areas of the *diamond-shaped* face, apply highlighter across your forehead and down from your ear lobes across your jawline and chin. Blend carefully.

To make the contour of the *round* face appear to recede, begin by applying highlighter down the centre of your face. Second, apply shadow to slim the outer edges, commencing at the beginning of your temples, and continuing down past your cheekbones, bringing the shadow inwards to the middle of your cheek. Blend downwards over your jawline. Apply highlighter at the top of your chin in line with the centre of your forehead.

Diamond-shaped Face

A person with a diamond-shaped face has high cheekbones with a narrow forehead and jawline. The objective is to create width on the forehead and jawline, while slimming the outer points of the cheekbones. For hints on creative make-up see illustration (above).

To counteract the angular feeling of this face shape, keep your eyebrows short and slightly rounded. Your lip line should be kept shorter than normal with a softer, slightly rounded upper lip.

Round Face

The round face has a rounded hair line, cheeks and chin. It has the shape of a ball with the ear lobes being the widest point, and is somewhat short in comparison to its width. For hints on creative make-up see illustration (above).

Eyebrows should be kept fairly straight or slightly angled. Extend them lightly beyond the normal point and keep the ends pointing to the sides. Your lip line should be made full, although your bottom lip should be less full.

Foundation

A good foundation provides a natural-looking protective film, smoothes out any uneven colouring and covers minor blemishes, projecting a flawless-looking skin. Choosing a foundation that is the right colour for you is made easy by following the skin colours to which you matched your skin.

Application

Foundation should always be applied with a light touch. Use your fingertips, or a dampened make-up sponge. First use a concealer or a lighter shade of foundation to cover dark circles or blemishes. Keep the coating extremely thin in the area under the eyes. Do not try to cover shadows completely as heavy make-up will only accentuate them. Let the foundation set for three to four minutes and then blot the excess with a tissue.

When shading and highlighting (see page 82) be sure to blend the shading well in the areas where it meets the foundation so there is no visible line. Shading can be quite dark towards the outside of the cheek or forehead, provided that it is blended well. You may also use shading under the jawline and along the chin to make the face stand out. Care must be taken here, as making the upper jaw too dark can result in some people's neck area looking grubby. Light foundation can be used in the eye area or towards the middle of the face and will also help to hide deep lines, dark circles, and minor blemishes.

RECEDING CHIN
Apply highlighter
across the chin line,
blending it under the
jaw.

DOUBLE CHIN
Apply shadow across
the lower part of the
chin, blending it under
the jaw.

PROTUDING CHIN
Highlight the area
around the mouth to
make the chin look as
if it is receding.

POINTED CHIN
Highlight both sides of
the pointed chin and
shadow the tip.

RECEDING FOREHEAD
Apply highlighter
straight across the
forehead, blending it
into the hairline.

PROTRUDING
FOREHEAD
Apply shadow straight
across the bulging part
of the forehead and
blend into the hairline.

Receding Chin

Double Chin

Protruding Chin

Pointed Chin

Receding Forehead

Protruding Forehead

*The Complete
Colour,
Style & Image
Book*

BROAD NOSE
To make this type of
nose appear narrower
in width, highlight
down the centre from
the bridge to the tip,
then shadow on either
side to create a 'dia-
mond' pattern of
correction.

Broad Nose

PROTRUDING BRIDGE
Shadow down the
length of the bridge
and highlight on either
side. Be careful not to
bring the highlighter
over the nostrils

Protruding Bridge

LONG NOSE
To cut down the appar-
ent length of a nose,
apply shadow on the
tip, blending it under
the nose.

Long Nose

UPTURNED NOSE
Apply highlighter
straight down the cen-
tre from the bridge of
the nose to under the
tip, then shadow the
turned-up portion and
blend downwards.

Upturned Nose

PROMINENT NOSE

If the nose has none of the distinct character-istics described above but it is nevertheless prominent, apply high-lighter starting from either side of the nose and extending to just beneath the middle of the eye. This will make the nose appear to recede, thereby making it less conspicuous.

Prominent Nose

SHORT NOSE

To give illusion of greater length, apply highlighter straight down the centre from the bridge of the nose to under the tip. Pluck eyebrows to give a wider space between them and a longer line to the nose.

Short Nose

CURVED BRIDGE

Apply shadow to the high point of the curve, then carefully blend highlighter both above and below the shad-owed area.

Curved Bridge

Oval Face

Round Face

Blusher

OVAL FACE
Apply blusher high on the cheekbone in a tri-angular shape, and blend into the hairline.

DIAMOND-SHAPED FACE
Apply blusher in a wedge-like pattern on the highest point of the cheekbone, being care-ful not to blend the blusher into the hollow of the cheeks.

ROUND FACE
Apply blusher in a wide triangular pat-tern, blending into the hairline and over the earlobe.

Blusher adds colour and definition to the face, and is an important part of every woman's complete make-up look. If you have a rosy complexion, you may think you do not need blusher. Look closely at your face, however, and you will probably notice that the pink is located on or around the nose, forehead or chin.

There are a few rules for applying blusher that apply to all face shapes. Never bring the blusher further across your cheek than below the mid point of the eye. It should never be applied higher than the corner of the eye, or lower than the nostril. For the most flattering effect, there are further rules that apply to each face shape face. A basic blusher 'place-ment' for each face shape is described and illustrated here.

Powder

Whatever your face shape, you should always apply powder over your founda-tion in order to 'set' it. Using a dry

Diamond-shaped Face

sponge, apply translucent powder over your face to create an invisible 'glove'. This will 'set' your make-up without changing the colour, and will keep it looking fresh for several hours. With the other side of the sponge, remove any excess visible powder with gentle brush-ing strokes, working downwards from the top of the face.

Rectangular Face

Pear-shaped Face

Square Face

Heart-shaped Face

RECTANGULAR FACE
Apply blusher high on the cheekbone in a rectangular pattern, keeping it very narrow. Do not run the blusher down the length of the face.

PEAR-SHAPED FACE
Apply blusher in a wide triangular pattern. Do not blend the blusher close to the nose area.

HEART-SHAPED FACE
Apply blusher in a narrow wedge-like pattern on the highest point of the cheekbone.

SQUARE FACE
Create a wide triangular pattern on the cheekbone. Blend downwards over the earlobe.

Eyebrows

The eyebrow is one of your most important facial features because it serves several purposes as far as your appearance is concerned. Firstly, it is a frame for the eye itself. Just as you want a frame to enhance a picture and yet not take anything away from its beauty, so your eyebrow should enhance your eye. Secondly, it adds to your expression, making you look alert and enlarging the eye area. Thirdly, it should balance the rest of your features.

If you have been blessed with well-shaped eybrows, which balance and enhance your face shape, then lightly brush them into the shape indicated for your face shape. As a general rule your eyebrow should begin at the inner corner of your eye (see next page). The highest point, called the arch, should be above the iris . To locate where your brow should begin, hold a pencil vertically by the side of your nose with one end touching the nostril – the other end should indicate where your brow should begin. Now hold the pencil diagonally at 45° from your nostril. The end of the pencil will indicate where your brow should end.

Here are a few guidelines for enhancing your eyebrows. Before you begin, please note that you should pencil your eyebrows only if necessary (see point 2, below), and that your eyebrow colour should match that of your hair.

1) Brush your brows outwards and upwards towards the highest point of the arch. Brush the tail of your brow outwards towards the temple to give fullness in this area.
2) If your brows are extremely sparse or light you may need to use a pencil. Use it *carefully* and *sparingly*. Try using two shades of pencil, both fairly light in colour; use a brown pencil (*not* black) just a shade darker than your hair, and a charcoal or light-grey pencil (depending on your hair colour). Never *draw* a line on your brow as the pencil is supposed to *fill*, not to form your entire brow line.
3) A wood-cased brow pencil should be sharpened to a flat blade edge, and an automatic pencil to a short, sharp point.
4) The start of your brow should be pencilled *lightly* because here the brow is usually sparse and should not look heavy.
5) Pencil in your brow with small, hair-like strokes in a diagonal, upwards direction to the highest point of the arch above the edge of the iris. Beyond this point, gradually start to shorten your strokes, going from upwards to outwards, in almost horizontal strokes, bringing the lines out towards the temple.
6) Keep the width of your brow almost

the same from the inner tip to the highest point of the natural arch; taper your brow only slightly on the outer side of the arch. *Your brow must never become too fine a line.*

7) After pencilling, smudge the brows lightly with the finger to blend the line and then brush your brow hairs to blend with the pencilling.

8) Avoid ending your brows in a steep downwards curve, plucking them too thinly or hooking them too far in towards the eye at the inner tip. Also avoid bushiness, an unkempt look, an exaggerated arch or too round an arch, the latter creating a look of surprise.

9) If you need to pluck your brows, use a pair of tweezers and pluck each hair in the direction it grows. To make the task less painful, place an ice cube in a paper tissue and hold on the area to be plucked for a few seconds before starting.

10) If you find it difficult to draw your brows lightly, rest your elbow on a table, hold the brow pencil as you would hold a pen, and then rest the little finger against the cheek for firm support as you make light, feathery strokes.

11) Remember that experimentation and practice makes perfect! Following the above rules should help you to achieve a *natural* yet beautiful arch in your brows.

As with make-up, eyebrows need to be treated differently according to the face shape in question. Guidelines for various face shapes and features are given on next page.

You should work out where your eyebrow should begin and end before starting to shape it.

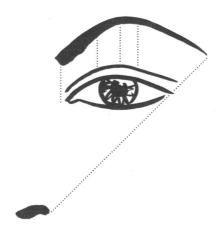

Balanced Oval Face

Here the forehead is in good proportion to the rest of the face, being neither too wide nor too narrow.

1) **Begin your brow at the inner corner of the eye.**
2) **Extend it to the highest point, which is directly above the iris of the eye.**
3) **Finish with a line equal in distance to the line from the beginning to the highest point.**

Wide Forehead

To create the illusion of less width:

1) **Begin your brow a bit closer to the nose than the inner corner of the eye.**
2) **Extend it to the highest point, which is directly above the inner iris of the eye.**
3) **Finish with a line equal in distance to the line from the beginning to the highest point.**

Narrow forehead

To create the illusion of more width:

1) **Begin your brow slightly outwards from the inner corner of the eye.**
2) **Extend to the highest point, which is directly above the outer corner of the iris of the eye.**
3) **The line from the highest point to the end should be short, no more than half the length of the line from the beginning to the highest point.**

Eyeliner

Eyeliner, available in either liquid or pencil form, is used to accentuate the eyes, effectively making them larger and improving their shape. The basic dark shades of black and brown intensify the eye colour and add length to the lashes. Bear in mind, however, that not everyone should wear eyeliner all around the eye area, particularly those with very small lids and deep-set eyes.

Like the face, the shape of the eyes differs from person to person. To achieve the eye effects most complementary to you, you must learn to experiment with eyeliners. It is fun to try out a large selection in colours that blend with each outfit and harmonize or match the colours of the eyes. Trends change, and colours come and go, so keep up to date by reading fashion and beauty magazines.

If you are using an eyeliner pencil, hold the flesh taut at the outer corner and draw a fine line as close to the lashes as possible. If you have well-spaced eyes, you should follow the contour of the upper and lower eyelid from the inner to the outer corner. Dotting the lower lid is much more natural and flattering than lining it. But if you do use a line, draw it very fine and apply it close to and underneath the lashes, smudging it slightly.

Some eyeshadows make excellent eyeliners as well, which gives you a larger choice of colours. To apply eyeshadow as liner, wet an eyeliner brush with alcohol-free toner to liquefy a corner of your chosen shadow. Apply as before and smudge.

Eyeshadow

The purpose of eye shadow is to emphasize the beauty of your eye area and to intensify the colour of your eyes. It may also be used to create the illusion of depth or to correct the contour of your eyes. Like eyeliner, eyeshadow can harmonize or contrast with the colour of your outfit.

All woman can use many colours of eye shadow. There are, however, a few general guidelines which can help you with your selection. If you have dark eyes, use an eyeshadow to blend with your outfit. If you have blue, green or hazel eyes, use an eyeshadow to intensify the colour of your iris or, if you prefer, to blend with your outfit. More detailed tips for each eye colour are given below.

A basic rule to remember is that light-coloured eyeshadows highlight areas, whereas dark ones create contours and shadow areas. Light-coloured eyeshadow is also used under dark eyeshadow to create a softer tone. Brown, navy and grey eyeshadows are used to diminish protruding contours. Deeper colour is usually more flattering when applied closest to the lashes with a subdued, greyed-down background (the protruding eye area and the crease).

Apply light shades on areas you want to bring forward, and use the darker shades on the areas you want to recede. For example, use the darker shades on the creases and outer lid, medium shades on the lids, and lighter shades on the brow bone and inner lid. Remember that eyeshadow should emphasize the eyes, not the shadow.

If you have eyeshadows which are too bright, try adding a little of their complementary colour to tone them down. With electric blue, for example, add a little orange. The results will amaze you.

Brown Eyes

People with brown eyes have great flexibility when it comes to eyeshadow colour. They can wear a wide variety, from greyed-down lavender, mauve, peach, coral, and olive to brown. Let the intensity of the eye colour guide you in how light or dark you should go.

Hazel Eyes

Although true hazel is a yellow-brown colour, hazel eyes often contain other colours, and therefore come in the following shades: blue-hazel, green-hazel, grey-hazel and brown-hazel. The colour will change with the colour of the clothes you wear, your environment and the colours with which you surround your eyes. Use your magnifying glass to pick out your second and third eye colours, or use smoky colours and neutrals which contain mixtures of the eye colours. Underline your eyes with one of the colours in your eyes to change the appearance of your eye colour at will.

Green Eyes

For warm greens, go for colours with a warm undertone or complementary colour. For cool greens, go for muted mauve, rose and lavender and avoid bright green.

Blue Eyes

Blue can look good when it is slightly muted or toned down. Bright-blue shadows which take over are wrong. Blue eyes with yellow in them can look good with peaches, gold and bronzes. The cooler-looking blue eyes also look good with greys, blue-grey and plum.

Corrective Measures for Eyes

Eyes Too Close Together

Try to create an illusion of a larger separation between the eyes. The brows should be started further out than the normal inner corner. If the shape of your face permits, try to keep your brow lines straighter than the classic brow shape previously explained, with not so much 'arch'.

Eyeliner should commence in line with the inner edge of the iris of the upper lid and be taken to the outer edge of the eye. Line the lower lid only at the outer corner. Use a lighter shade of eyeshadow on the inner eye area, shading darker towards the outer edge of the lid.

If further illusion of separation is needed, extend the brow to, but never beyond, the outer corner. Eyeshadow should be blended so that it appears deeper on the far side of the lids, away from the nose. This will give an illusion of width.

Eyes Too Far Apart

Start your eyebrows further in towards the bridge of the nose. Keep them rather short, unless the forehead is excessively wide. Eyeliner should commence at the inner corner of the upper lid and stop before it reaches the outer corner. Treat the lower lid similarly if you wish. Eyeshadow should be used to darken the crease on inside corners and should be applied to the entire lid.

Protruding Eyes

You should try to draw attention away from the wide space between the eyebrow line and the eyelid. This can be accomplished in two ways – either by lowering the eyebrow line as much as possible for a heavier brow, or by raising the eyebrow line up as far as possible to lift the onlooker's gaze above the bulging eyelid. Test with a pencil to see which suits you best. Bear in mind that the brow should never be beneath the bone which you can feel above your eye.

Eyeliner can focus attention on the middle of the eye. On the upper lid, start the line back from the inner corner and end it before it reaches the outer corner. You can line or dot the entire lower lid, but apply the line or dots on the ridge above the lashes.

With eyeshadow, the eye will be visibly reduced in size if only a matte or muted shade is used. Grey and brown are ideal for this eye type. Apply shadow away from the inner corner and stop it before reaching the outer corner. Keep the intensity of the colour in the centre of the eye. Fade shadow up to meet the eyebrow line, being careful not to use too much colour which will attract attention to the eyelid.

Deep-set eyes

Correction is needed in order to give the illusion of greater space between the eyebrow and eyelid. This is accomplished by raising the brow as high as possible and giving it a high arch. Eyeliner must be applied very thinly. Start almost in the middle of the upper eyelid and draw the line all the way to the end. Never add an extending line as this will only make your eye look harsh and will draw attention to your make-up rather than to your eyes. It is best in most cases of deep-set eyes to eliminate dark eyeliners altogether and stick to light colours.

To define the eye, use a light eyeshadow to highlight the entire lid, tapering the shadow around the outer edge of the eye, and under the corner of the bottom lid. Use a white eyeliner pencil to line the inner eyelid, gently pressing the lower lid with the fingers of one hand while you line just above the eyelashes with the other hand. Use a darker, muted shade on the crease, along the underside of the orbital bone, making the eye appear more almond-shaped. Apply mascara to the lashes.

Round Eyes

Eyebrows should be extended and a steeper arch created. Use eyeliner on the lower lid, and extend the line lower and further outwards at the outside corner of the eye. Line the upper lid upwards and outwards. Use eyeshadow on the outer corner of the eye. Add highlighter to the outer portion of the browbone and above the crease towards the brow tip.

Oriental Eyes

Where more dimension is required, draw in a crease above the natural one with a dark, muted shade. Apply eyeliner to the lower lid, even lower than normal. To make the eyes appear larger, apply highlighter to the brow bone to make it more prominent and divide the eye area into three equal parts.

Small Eyes

If you have small eyes you need to extend the eyebrows to give a feeling of size. You also need to use eyeliner on the entire eyelid and a lighter shade on the lower lid. Use eyeshadow close to the upper lashes and blend it out slightly at the outer corners.

Down-slanting Eyes

If you have down-slanting eyes you need to create 'lift'. You can do this by sloping and gently tapering the outer half of the brow from the high point to the outer corner towards the hair line, then applying eyeliner on the upper lid at the outer corner. Apply liner to the lower lid even lower than the norm at the centre of the eye. Also apply a dark inner eyeliner on the lower lid at the outer corner. Angle both eyeliner and eyeshadow upwards at the outer corner.

Mascara

To make the eye appear larger, apply mascara on both the upper and lower lashes. Apply the mascara so that your lashes are evenly coated from roots to tip. Brush the lashes with an eyelash separator and then apply a second coat. When you are applying complete make-up, mascara is always applied after eyeliner.

Lipliner

You can use lipliner to make your upper lip appear fuller. Shape it so that it is as full as your lower lip, and make the middle dip of the bow more shallow. Extend the tips of the bow and the outer corners of the lips. Pencil a line between the two, slightly extending the bow line as you progress to the outside corner of the mouth. This will make your upper lip more rounded and full. Bring the corner of your lower lip out to meet the corners of your upper lip line.

If your lips are thick, keep the outline within the natural form of the mouth. If your lips are thin, keep the line as full as possible while following the natural line of the mouth. Remember, your lipliner should blend with your lipstick.

Applying Make-up to the Mouth

You can reshape your mouth using cosmetics to give an appearance of fullness and contour. The first step is to outline the lips using either a pencil or lip brush. Choose a medium or bright shade for your outline, and a lipstick one shade paler to 'colour in' your lips. Bear in mind, though, that the two colours should blend, and that contrasting colours will not work.

If you use a lip brush, choose a soft, sable-tipped one. A brush gives a smoother finish as it fills in the lip cracks and makes the lipstick last longer. Saturate the brush with colour to make it easier to apply. Hold the brush as you would a pencil; place your elbow on a table and rest the little finger against the chin to act as a pivot.

Let lipstick colour set for three minutes or longer and then blot with a tissue to prevent feathering. To help it stay on longer, apply lipstick once, blot, reapply and blot again. For a natural dewy look, apply lip gloss.

Experiment with shaping and colouring to achieve a natural lip line. The following guidelines will help you get the best out of your particular lip shape:

Normal Lip Line
Fill the bristle of the brush with lipstick, and follow the natural outline.

Lower Lip Too Full
Follow the natural contour of your lower lip, then apply the line inside the normal lipline. Fill in and blot well.

Mouth Too Thin
Draw a line both slightly above and below the normal lip line. Fill in.

Mouth Too Narrow
With a lipliner extend the corners of the mouth on both sides, tapering to a graceful point.

Drooping Mouth
Lift each corner on both upper and lower lip until it meets the natural lipline. Fill in.

Irregular Lip Line
With your pencil or brush, raise the low side and lower the high side to balance the entire mouth.

Chapter 7

BODY BALANCE

An essential part of looking your best is taking care of your inner self, because how you feel on the inside shows on the outside. This chapter looks at the importance of leading a balanced, healthy lifestyle.

Do You Lead a Balanced Lifestyle?

A balanced person with plenty of energy for the lifestyle she leads can cope with the ups and downs life throws at her. She has healthy eating and drinking habits, and does not have cravings for junk food or addictive substances such as cigarettes and alcohol. A person who falls into this category has already worked out how to maintain balance in her system either by trial and error or by being aware and trusting her own instincts and common sense.

If you are fortunate enough to be this type of balanced individual, then you will have a positive self-image and attitude to life in general. Perhaps, however, you are one of the many people who makes some concessions to healthy living, but feels that the effort and sacrifices required to achieve such a balanced system make it an impossible dream. Perhaps your view is that, in your busy, stressful lifestyle, there is no time to 'be perfect'. It is easy to come up with an excuse. We are all capable of changing our inner selves, but first we have to change the way in which we think.

Many people often imagine that improving their body and mind means a total revamp from top to bottom, starting with long stressful exercise or living on a lettuce leaf. This could not be further from the truth. More often than not it turns out that the changes you need to make are relatively small and involve only slight adjustments. In addition, the knowledge you have gained of your personal colouring and figure shape puts you ahead of most others. Now you are familiar with personal analysis you can decide which areas you wish to improve and then make the necessary adjustments to give you the results you want.

Be the Best You Can Be

Each of us is biochemically unique, and the proteins that make up your body tissues are uniquely yours. In the same way as no one clothing or shoe size will fit everyone, there is no single dietary programme that will meet every individual's metabolic needs. Each body requires a slightly different approach and a different blend of nutritional components. These metabolic differences are regulated by our glands, which control how fast or how slow we burn off calories, the sort of foods we crave, how much weight we put on and where, and how much of the same weight we will lose if we diet. The major glands involved in this process are the pituitary, thyroid, adrenal and gonadal glands.

Studies have shown that losing weight is not just a case of reducing calories and increasing activity. If your glandular system does not act to balance your metabolism and remove the undesirable weight, then the effect of any dietary programme will not last and you could end up heavier and more imbalanced than before. The function of the glandular system must therefore be taken into account in any long-term weight plan.

The system of glandular typing to balance your metabolism was developed by Dr Henry G. Bieler, a pioneer in the field of nutritional health care, and was further expanded by Dr Elliot D. Abravanal. Some practical further research in which I have been involved has shown that where there are weight problems there is usually an accompanying imbalance in the glandular system. I have also found it fascinating to learn that individuals with similar body types often share specific dietary preferences, food cravings, preferred activities and personal traits.

The guidelines below should be followed within a balanced diet. If the recommendations for your body type include cutting down on fruit, then this should be replaced with extra salad or vegetables. If you need to cut down on dairy products, then include more fish, poultry, lean meat, beans or supplementary soya protein. If you cut down on refined carbohydrates, it is important to replace them with whole grains as you need less of these to satisfy your intake of dietary fibre. For additional fibre you can also add more coloured vegetables.

When the term 'eat freely' is used, it means that balanced proportions are recommended. 'Eat moderately' means cut down on the amount of the food type you are eating at the moment. And 'eat sparingly' means reduce your intake so that the food is eaten no more than twice each week.

Food Guidelines for Different Body Types

Complete the following questionnaire to discover which gland type you are. Then study the chart on page 101, which gives further information on your type – your physical features, the foods you crave and other characteristics.

The Complete Colour, Style & Image Book

For each question, pick the answer that most applies to you, then circle the number to the right of the answer. Now add up the points scored in each column. The column with the highest score is most likely your body type. Look at the bottom of each column to find out what this type is.

Questionnaire

	Gonadal	Adrenal	Thyroid	Pituitary
1. When you look at yourself straight on in a mirror, describe the overall shape or outline of your body.				
a. At least a full size larger below the waist.	2			
b. Stocky and/or full-figured with almost no waist or hip definition.		2		
c. Curvy, with waist, hips and upper thighs tending to be heavy while extremities are slender.			2	
d. Rather childlike, with small breasts and fat distributed evenly over the whole body.				2
2. Look at your profile, focusing on the line of your back. Which of the following best describes what you see?				
a. Back slightly curved with prominent buttocks.	2			
b. Back straight with flat buttocks.		2		
c. Lower back straight with rounded, but not especially prominent, buttocks.			2	
d. Round shoulders with forward-leaning head and small, childlike buttocks.				2
3. Describe your body when you are at your ideal weight.				
a. Slim, but with rounded hips and buttocks.	2			
b. Slender, yet full-figured; appearing to be sturdily built.		2		
c. Very slender and fine-boned.			2	
d. Slender, childlike, rather underdeveloped.				2
4. Looking at your body from the front, where is your excess weight located?				
a. On your buttocks and thighs.	2			
b. On the upper part of your body (upper back, stomach).		2		
c. In the middle of your body (waist, hips, upper thighs).			2	
d. All over your body, with no specific location.				2
5. Looking at your body from the back, where is your excess weight located?				
a. Below your waist.	2			
b. Across your upper back.		2		
c. Around your waist.			2	
d. All over your body, with no specific location.				2
6. Do you have saddlebags (pockets of fat on outer thighs)?				
a. Yes (circle both numbers on this line).	1		1	
b. No (circle both numbers on this line).		1		1
7. Describe your legs.				
a. Heavy.	2			
b. Muscular.		2		
c. Relatively thin.			2	
d. Short, chubby.				2
8. Do your hands have an accumulation of fat?				
a. Yes (circle both numbers on this line).		1	1	
b. No (circle both numbers on this line).	1		1	
TOTAL				
	Gonadal	Adrenal	Thyroid	Pituitary

Each body type tends to crave the kinds of foods that stimulate their dominant gland. To bring balance to the glandular system, it is necessary to reduce the intake of those foods and eat more of the foods which enhance the actions of the other glands. To enable you to do this, consult the following list. This tells you which foods each body type may eat freely, moderately and sparingly – and the foods to be avoided completely.

While following these guidelines, it is also extremely important for all body types to consume six to eight glasses of natural spring water every day to flush the toxins out of the system. Regular exercise – ideally three times a week – is essential too. If you have been fairly inactive for a while, start by exercising gently. Regular walking, for example, is a perfect start. Fitter types may find that an extra exercise session works wonders. Remember, it is down to you – decide which areas you wish to improve and then make the necessary adjustments to give you the results you want.

Once you have found out which body type you are, this chart gives you further information.

Body Type	Physical Features	Food Cravings	Energy Levels	Personal Tendencies	Common Health Conditions
THYROID *Narrow* Straight Curvy Ellipse Angular	Round shoulders; graceful, long neck; long, thin arms and legs; finely moulded, graceful hands; beautiful fingers; delicate features; fine bones; pot belly; spare tyre when overweight.	Sweets of all kinds, breads, cakes, pastries, caffeine.	Sleeps 6-7 hours when feeling good; 9-10 hours when tired. Highest energy after eating. "Race-horse" metabolism. Quick, restless, on the go.	Intellectual; loves words and conversation; changeable and lively; sensitive and artistic; enjoys travel and change.	Cold/sinus trouble; skin eruptions; fatigue/variable energy; poor circulation (cold hands and feet); stomach troubles.
ADRENAL *Broad* Straight Curvy Ellipse Heart Pituitary	Square or round head; short, thick neck; broad chest (men); large bust (women); thick trunk; short, thick fingers; solid build; big-boned; coarse features.	Steak, meat, salty foods, peanuts.	Sleeps 6-8 hours. Good energy all day long. Excellent endurance. Slow but steady.	Hard worker; amiable; sociable; warm; friendly; slow to anger; not easy to push around; steady; stable; practical.	'Cast-iron' stomach; perspires easily; lower backache; trouble sleeping; weight problems; seldom catches a cold.
PITUITARY *Underdeveloped* Straight Curvy Ellipse Angular	Large head in proportion to body; round, sloping shoulders; small breasted (women); small rear end; small stature; looks younger than age; often has childlike 'puppy fat' all over.	Dairy products, ice cream, yoghurt.	Sleeps 7-8 hours. Highest energy in the morning.	Intellectual; curious; very idealistic; philosophical.	Mental obsession; stress; weak digestion; chronic allergies; headaches; weak joints.
GONADAL *Unbalanced* Straight Curvy Pear	Curved back; saddle bags; large rear end; bottom half larger than top; weight on hips and thighs.	Rich or spicy foods, creamy foods and sauces.	Sleeps 7-9 hours; seldom has trouble sleeping. Energy highest later in the day.	Motherly; nurturing; magnetic; warm; friendly; needs lots of close relationships; enjoys crafts and cooking.	Feet swell and ache; bladder infections; first-day menstrual cramps.

Healthy Balance for Pituitary Types

EAT FREELY

- **beef, lamb and pork (without visible fat)**
- **organ meats (liver, kidney and heart)**
- **fish**
- **poultry**
- **alternative sources of complete vegetable protein**
- **fresh vegetables (raw or cooked – all coloured fresh vegetables make ideal snacks)**

MODERATE AMOUNTS

- **eggs**
- **all fruit**
- **wholegrains**
- **skimmed milk**
- **olive oil**
- **coffee (preferably decaffeinated)**

HARDLY EVER

- **butter**
- **cheese**
- **cream**
- **desserts**
- **refined carbohydrates**
- **yoghurt**
- **tea**

MENU SUGGESTIONS

Breakfast

- **two eggs**
- **kidneys or fish**
- **wholegrain bread**

Lunch

- **mixed vegetables**
- **some potatoes or a large salad**
- **meat or fish**
- **small portion of wholegrain bread**

Dinner

- **fish or poultry (or meat)**
- **cooked or raw vegetables**
- **small, light dessert or fresh fruit**

Healthy Balance for Thyroid Types

EAT FREELY
- eggs
- fish
- poultry
- low-fat cheese
- alternative sources of complete vegetable protein
- light dairy products
- fresh vegetables (raw or cooked – all coloured fresh vegetables make ideal snacks)

MODERATE AMOUNTS
- butter
- full-fat cheese
- fruit
- lean red meat
- olive oil
- wholegrains

HARDLY EVER
- chocolate and sweets
- tea and coffee (and other sources of caffeine)
- desserts
- pasta and refined starches (white flour, sugar)

MENU SUGGESTIONS
Breakfast
- any good source of protein (such as boiled eggs)
- one slice of wholegrain bread
- decaffeinated coffee

Lunch
- chicken, fish, meat or cottage cheese
- large, green salad (can include raw vegetables)
- one slice of wholegrain bread
- one piece of fruit
- decaffeinated coffee or herbal tea

Dinner
- fish, poultry or (twice a week only) meat
- green, orange, red or yellow vegetables (raw or cooked)

Healthy Balance for Adrenal Types

EAT FREELY
- **low-fat cheese**
- **cottage cheese**
- **fish**
- **low-fat yoghurt**
- **skimmed milk**
- **fresh vegetables, except potatoes (raw or cooked – all coloured fresh vegetables make ideal snacks)**
- **whole grains**

MODERATE AMOUNTS
- **desserts (only twice per week)**
- **fruit**
- **poultry**
- **potatoes**
- **stir-fried coloured vegetables with fish or poultry in olive oil**

HARDLY EVER
- **butter**
- **Cheddar or other high-fat cheeses**
- **red meat**
- **nuts**

MENU SUGGESTIONS
Breakfast
- **light, whole-grain porridge/cereal or low-fat yoghurt**
- **tea or coffee**

Lunch
- **small amount of low-fat cheese or a vegetarian dish**
- **large salad with red, orange, yellow and green vegetables**
- **two slices of wholegrain bread**
- **tea and coffee**

Dinner
- **fish or poultry (or red meat but no more than twice a week)**
- **unlimited vegetables (raw or cooked)**
- **whole-grain rice**
- **fruit or a light dessert**
- **decaffeinated coffee or tea**

Healthy Balance for Gonadal Types

EAT FREELY

- **fresh vegetables (raw and cooked – all coloured fresh vegetables make ideal snacks)**
- **fruit**
- **fish**
- **low-fat cottage cheese**
- **milk and yoghurt**

MODERATE AMOUNTS

- **red meat**
- **olive oil (for stir-frying)**
- **coffee or tea**

HARDLY EVER

- **butter**
- **chocolate**
- **creamy foods and sauces**
- **ice cream and rich desserts**
- **spices and condiments**

MENU SUGGESTIONS

Breakfast

- **fruit**
- **low-fat yoghurt**

Lunch

- **large salad with red, orange, yellow and green vegetables**
- **low-fat cheese**
- **brown rice or wholegrain bread**
- **one piece of fruit**

Dinner

- **fish or poultry**
- **lots of mixed vegetables (raw or cooked)**
- **a piece of fruit or a light dessert**
- **decaffeinated coffee or tea**

Choice Matters

Studies indicate that our minds are affected by complex chemical processes. Through nourishing your glands correctly you can influence the way in which you feel and respond. Instead of succumbing to the foods you crave, you can consciously make the foods you eat work *for* you instead of against you.

Take as an example the case of John Hinckley who shot President Reagan. His addiction to beefburgers, cola drinks and television 'nasties' was cited in his case as creating his diminished responsibility, and was said to have saved him from the electric chair.

Being open to the possibility that you can make profound changes to your health, energy levels and reaction to life events gives you the choice to see yourself as you want to be. You can define your new reality and can choose to see yourself getting younger, slimmer and more vibrant.

Eating healthily in order to balance your glands requires self-discipline. The psychological problem will be the abrupt eliminating of some foods or drinks from your diet which can leave a real emotional or social gap in your life. Think it through. You do not 'have' to drink caffeinated coffee or tea at break time, alcohol when you socialize or desserts to round off a meal. Many people, however,

are addicted to certain foods and drinks. Caffeine is a prime example. Cutting it out abruptly can lead to headaches. If this happens to you, try following the method I used to cut down, which is described on following page (see step 2).

Keep your goal in mind – looking and feeling good, and gaining more energy, better health, confidence and self-control. You will find that you can lose weight without counting calories or going hungry.

Talk to Yourself

As you progress in your new, healthier lifestyle, give yourself positive feedback. Talk to yourself and become aware of what you are saying. Let your body know how you want to behave and programme it for positive results.

These self-chats are extremely important. They can have a tremendous impact on your life. How many times, for instance, do you say negative or even nasty things to yourself? If you do this often, you are effectively burying negative thoughts deeper and deeper into your subconscious. Start to become aware of your thoughts and listen closely to what you are saying to yourself. Think of the positive outcome and not of scolding yourself for eating forbidden foods. Such self-criticism is programming both your

Ten Steps to Healthy Living

1) SET A GOAL. It is well known that the highest achievers are people who have a sense of responsibility and are in control of their lives. One of the best ways to help you reinforce this is to set specific goals that you can measure.

2) DEFINE YOUR GOAL. Goals have to be defined and not just wishful thinking. Plan to be at a definite point in three months' time. One of my goals, for example, was to give up caffeinated coffee and tea in a month. I defined my goal by breaking it down into stages. First, I mixed a tin of coffee half and half with decaffeinated and my regular caffeinated brand. Next, I reduced the amount of caffeinated coffee to a quarter. Finally, I drank only decaffeinated coffee or herbal beverages (coffee substitutes) when I was out. To assist, I was already drinking tomato juice and mineral water with lemon – and liking it.

3) SET TIME ASIDE. You need to allot time to carry out specific tasks. Spend a morning cleaning out your cupboards of all the foods you should eat sparingly (save the eating of these types of food for when you go out on a special occasion).

4) CHANGE YOUR SHOPPING HABITS. Start to fill your cupboards with foods you can eat any time.

5) INVOLVE OTHERS. Get other members of your household involved in a self-improvement programme. This will help you and them.

6) REWARD YOURSELF. Plan a reward for yourself or get other family members to have a wager with you. For example, my husband and daughter bet me £50 each that I could not give up caffeinated coffee.

7) IDENTIFY POOR EATING HABITS. These might include not sitting down to eat, eating whilst watching television or going shopping when you are hungry, which is stretching temptation too far.

8) KEEP TABS ON YOUR PROGRESS. If you should fail, give yourself a good talking to. Think it through and decide what put temptation in the way and how this can be avoided. Visualize a more positive outcome in case a similar situation arises again.

9) KEEP YOUR GOALS IN SIGHT. Make a list of your goals and keep them in front of you at all times. Enjoy the satisfaction of crossing them off once you have overcome your addiction.

10) THINK POSITIVE. Surround yourself with other positive-thinking people who have achieved or are achieving their goals. Read about people who have overcome adversity against all odds.

Two inspiring books are *Jonathan Livingstone Seagull* and *The Seven Summits.* The first is legendary, but the second not so well known. It is a story of three men who had a dream. This dream was as straightforward as it was difficult. They wanted to climb the highest mountain on each of the world's seven continents. No one had ever scaled all seven summits – how was that for a goal? This goal would be a first – a feat that had eluded the world's best mountaineers.

What made it all the more extraordinary was that two of the party were businessmen, not mountaineers. In the book they take you through the gruelling days when it seemed easier to quit, to the thrilling moments when a summit had been conquered.

brain and body to concentrate on the foods you need to forget.

To break bad habits, use a more positive statement such as 'I will put more colour on my plate and eat the food which will keep my glands in a healthy balance'. This is all part of developing a technique for making your brain think positively.

Focus Now!

The more you practise being totally focused on your goal, the more competent you will become and the quicker you will achieve it. Instead of dwelling on the past or on what may or may not happen tomorrow, use all your mental and emotional energy to focus on what you are working towards today. The only real time is the present. Yesterday has gone and tomorrow may never happen.

Make yourself believe that you are capable of achieving your goal. Accept as a foregone conclusion that, given time, you will attain it. Make sure your vocabulary is positive: 'I can, I will'. Think positively and believe in yourself. Set yourself a realistic goal. Surround yourself with colour. Invite the light force into your life and draw strength from it. See yourself successfully building up your lifestyle wardrobe and always having just the right outfit to wear.

If you desire more energy or a healthier lifestyle, visualize yourself enjoying a healthy diet and physically doing the necessary exercises. Imagine your wonderful new shape and your new found zest for life. Then do whatever has to be done to achieve your goal. Do not bury your head in the sand. Make no mistake about it – your mind controls your body. To quote a wise, old friend of mine, 'What you think you are, what you think you do, what you think you become'.

Chapter 8

COLOUR AND PERSONALITY

The light force we know as colour influences us in so many ways, including our moods, health and feelings. The psychological effects of colour are still little understood, but knowledge in this area is growing. There is much evidence to suggest that when the light force enters the eye it indirectly affects the centre of our emotions in our hypothalamus gland. This in turn affects the pituitary gland, the master gland that controls the entire endocrine system, and consequently our moods.

The psychology of colour goes back thousands of years. Various systems have been devised that use colour to assess people's personality traits. Such systems are designed to help us become more aware of colour and to understand the influence of colour in our lives. One of the systems I have used over the years is the Luscher colour test. As well as analysing personality, it can also give vocational guidance, and has been used in personnel selection for commerce and industry. You take the test by selecting colours in your order of preference. You then compare the colours you have chosen with the known personality attributes of that colour.

I have pioneered another method with the help of students of The Academy of Colour and Style International. This method takes the opposite approach to the Luscher test in that you are asked a series of questions about yourself. Your answers reveal your personality, which is then linked to the colour which matches it. The test which follows is easy to do, and it does not take much time. Why not try it? You will discover the mix of colours that make you tick and your colour personality.

Colour Personality Questionnaire

Carefully read through the following questions. If your answer is 'yes', tick the box next to the question. If your answer is 'no', or if you are unsure, leave the box blank. To get reliable results, it is important to be honest with yourself.

Acknowledge. Do you acknowledge others for their ideas and for their work? (7) ☐

Ambitious. Do you set goals and work towards them? (1) ☐

Appreciate. Do you appreciate how other people affect your life? (4) ☐

Artistic. Do you like creating things? (7) ☐

Assertive. Do others see you as being in control? (1) ☐

Awareness. Are you aware of and sensitive to other people's feelings? (5) ☐

Balanced. Do you have a balanced approach to work and play? (4) ☐

Carefree. Are you carefree, light-hearted and full of spirit? (3) ☐

Compassion. Do you have a desire to alleviate people's suffering? (6) ☐

Confidence. Do you have confidence, even when asked to do something a little out of the ordinary? Do you accept a challenge? (2) ☐

Considerate. Are you considerate and thoughtful towards other people? (8) ☐

Contented. Are you contented with your life? (4) ☐

Creative. In your social group or working environment are you the one who comes up with the good ideas that are acted upon? (7) ☐

Decisive. Are you decisive when everyone around you is dithering about a problem? Do you have the initiative to come up with a proposal and implement it? (1) ☐

Dedicated. Are you dedicated to a particular purpose or cause? (5) ☐

Dependable. Can others rely on you implicitly? (6) ☐

Dignity. Would others consider you to be dignified (7) ☐

Diplomatic. Are you diplomatic when dealing with other people? (5) ☐

Efficient. Are you organized? Do you work to a routine and pattern either at home or at work so that you can immediately lay your hands on anything you need at any given time? (5) ☐

Empathy. Do you try to understand other people's feelings? (8) ☐

Endurance. Have you the staying power to see a job through, even to the point of being a workaholic? (1) ☐

Energetic. Would you say you prefer to pursue energetic leisure activities? (2) ☐

Enliven. Do you try to brighten up a situation? Do you try to be cheerful? (7) ☐

Enthusiastic. Are you so enthusiastic that you also succeed in inspiring others with enthusiasm? (2) ☐

Even-tempered. Do you have a calming influence on others? (8) ☐

Friendly. Are you one of the first to approach a new colleague or neighbour to see if there is any help or information you can give? (3) ☐

Fun-loving. Are you a provider of enjoyment, amusement and gaiety? (3) ☐

Gentle. Are you gentle? (8) ☐

Good listener. Do people enjoy talking to you because they know you are listening to them? (8) ☐

Independent. Can you depend on your own ability to see a project through? (1) ☐
Instigator. Are you an instigator of action, amusement and gaiety? (2) ☐
Intuitive. Are you intuitive? (7) ☐
Judgement. Do others ask your opinion because they know you have good judgement? (4) ☐
Leader. Do you offer your services and take control? (1) ☐
Logical. Do you exercise clear valid reasoning? (4) ☐
Loyalty. Do you speak up for your friends and others when they are not there to defend themselves? (5) ☐
Maturity. Are you a person wiser than your years? (6) ☐
Modest. Are you modest about your achievements? (7) ☐
Open-minded. Are you open-minded in everything you do? (7) ☐
Opinionated. Are you opinionated? (4) ☐
Optimistic. When things are not going well, can you keep your spirits up by thinking positively? (3) ☐
Organization. When you are given the task of calling a meeting or arranging a trip, does everything run smoothly because you plan it well? (5) ☐
Outgoing. Are you a volunteer or often chosen as a group leader? (3) ☐
Party-goer. Are you the life and soul of a party? Do you enjoy contributing to make the party go with a swing? (2) ☐
Patient. Having given someone a task,

can you wait to see the results? (8) ☐
Receptive. Are you receptive to other people? (2) ☐
Relax. Are you able to empty your mind of mundane worries so that you can relax and appear totally calm? (6) ☐
Reliable. Are you reliable? (5) ☐
Respect. Do you show respect? (6) ☐
Responsibility. Do you like responsibility and power? (1) ☐
Self-assured. Are you self-assured? (2) ☐
Self-centred. Are you self-centred? (3) ☐
Self-control. Do you show self-control? (4) ☐
Self-discipline. When you bring work home in the evening can you easily get on without being distracted? (1) ☐
Share. Do you share your knowledge with others easily? (4) ☐
Spontaneous. Are you spontaneous? (3) ☐
Sympathetic. Do you find that you are often singled out for advice? (6) ☐
Thoughtful. Are you always aware when others around you are not feeling on top of the world and if so, do you help them through difficult patches? (5) ☐
Tolerance. Are you tolerant? (8) ☐
Trusting. Are you trusting of others? (3) ☐
Vivacious. Are you vivacious? (2) ☐
Well-behaved. Are you well-behaved? (8) ☐
Well-mannered. Are you well-mannered as a matter of course? (6) ☐
Yielding. Do you yield to others who are more stubborn than you? (6) ☐

How to Calculate Your Results

The moment of truth is here. Simply count how many boxes you have ticked that have a number (1) beside them. Enter the total at the side of colour (1) below in the positive (+) total column. Do the same with colours (2), (3), (4), (5), (6), (7) and (8).

These values represent your positive colour personality attributes. You can also discover your negative colour personality attributes – simply subtract from 8 the number you have entered in the positive (+) total column for each colour. Enter this total in the negative (–) total column for each colour.

1 = Red	(+)_____ (–)_____
2 = Orange	(+)_____(–)_____
3 = Yellow	(+)_____(–)_____
4 = Green	(+)_____(–)_____
5 = Blue	(+)_____(–)_____
6 = Indigo	(+)_____(–)_____
7 = Violet	(+)_____(–)_____
8 = White	(+)_____(–)_____

The colour with the highest positive score is your main personality colour. The colour with your next highest positive score is your second personality colour and so on. You will find that the colour with the highest negative score is the one most unlike your personality. Remember that you are a mix of different colours, so all the characteristics of your number one colour may not reflect your personality totally. The other colours will also influence your personality. But what do these colour personality attributes tell us about ourselves? The following is an analysis of each colour's personality.

RED

Red people are dominant thinkers and powerful leaders. They enjoy and value success and are willing to pay the price. Although they are independent individuals, they can enjoy teamwork, but only when they are the shining stars. They are dynamic, direct and highly resourceful. They enjoy a challenge and like to stay on top of things, and are fortunate in having a zest for life.

A good description of someone in this category would be that of an intense, impulsive and active achiever. Red people are exciting, animated, optimistic, emotional and extroverted. They have strong desires and live life to the full. Since they crave so much excitement, however, routine can drive them mad, and they can be very restless in their pursuit of new ideas or possessions. It is difficult for them to be objective, and they tend to be somewhat opinionated and impatient.

Red people will listen to advice but in the end they will do as they like anyway.

ORANGE

The physical energy of red and the mental energy of yellow give an orange person assertive mental energy and a tenacity for life. Orange people prefer energetic leisure activities and will work tirelessly until their objectives are accomplished. They are instigators of action, and full of contagious enthusiasm that makes any party go with a swing. They are good-natured, expansive and extroverted, with unique ideas and a strong determination to succeed, which they generally do. They would rather be agreeable than aggressive, but can be fickle – their latest friend is often their best friend.

YELLOW

Yellow people are carefree, light-hearted and full of spirit, bringing enjoyment, amusement and gaiety to others. They have candid expressions and inspire others into action. They are open, friendly individuals who have a zest for living life to the full, and whose ambitions are often realized.

People in this group are also positive thinkers who appreciate and value themselves and the world around them. Genuinely concerned about the good of society, they are also good with children.

They are highly original in their thinking – imaginative, idealistic, creative and artistic. With their inquiring minds, they love novelty and challenge. They can be generous, but rather shy and may appear somewhat aloof as a result. A yellow person may, however, be impatient with other people's ideas if they appear less well-thought-out than their own.

GREEN

Green people are often appreciated for their balanced judgement, valid reasoning and self-control. They like those around them to have a balanced approach to work and play. Although self-opinionated, they are willing to share their knowledge, and are thoughtful, generous and kind.

This blue/yellow personality mix brings stability with depth, sincerity and compassion. A green person makes a good citizen and a concerned parent who often gets involved in local activities. It is important for a green person to win the admiration of others and they are obsessed with doing the right thing. They make good, caring companions, and loyal friends or partners. They are intelligent and grasp new ideas quickly, but can be conservative, preferring to stick to conventional behaviour rather than trying something new. A green person often has a big appetite for food.

BLUE

Blue people are steady and enduring and like a sense of purpose to their life. They enjoy sharing intimate feelings with a companion and make an ongoing contribution to a relationship. Loyal and sincere, they seem to recognize when people around them are not feeling their best. They are also sensitive to the needs of others and often form strong attachments.

Blues strive hard to be perfectionists, but can also enjoy the accomplishments of others. They have excellent organizational skills, and can be relied upon to do a good job. They are very trusting and need to be trusted in return, and become deeply hurt if their trust is betrayed.

These people aspire to harmony, serenity, patience, perseverance and peace. They are socially reserved, often thinking twice before speaking, and usually prefer to stay within their own close circle of friends. Although generally even-tempered and reliable, blue people's perfectionism can get a bit out of hand because of their highly developed sense of responsibility. Their gentleness will, however, always win in the end.

INDIGO

Indigo people like contentment and a secure, safe, balanced existence. They often make concessions in their lifestyle to maintain the status quo. They never crave real excitement and do not like to attract attention to themselves, but they can get emotionally involved when they communicate. They are correct and well-mannered, and have tremendous empathy for other people's misfortunes. They are often singled out for advice as they are good listeners and have a dependable nature. Indigo people are mature, calm and relaxed. They are practical people willing to work hard and to be of service to others. They are the middle-of-the-road types, composed, cool and reliable.

VIOLET

This colour is often preferred by artists. All violet people are highly creative and often unconventional. Their artistic talents keep them from ever becoming bored, and they are the ones who come up with new ideas in brainstorming sessions. Despite their creativity, they have the ability to keep their ego under control, coupled with a strong sense of dignity and a cheerful disposition. They are often intuitive, generous and charming.

Violet is also associated with satire, good observation, sensitivity, vanity and moodiness. As violet is a combination of red and blue, which are opposite colours in many ways, these people often have conflicting characteristics, constantly trying to balance the excitement of red with the tranquillity of blue. It has been said that violet people are easy to live with but difficult to get to know.

WHITE

White types are contented and agreeable individuals, and very compatible with all other colour personalities. Their gentle diplomacy gathers them friends and has a calming influence on others. They are patient, moderate people without the strong extremes of the other colour personalities. Their equal balance of all the colours puts things in a proper perspective and makes them patient, down-to-earth leaders. They are givers, not takers, and as such are considerate, thoughtful and kind.

Building Your Character through Colour

We are born with our colour personality. It reflects our natural attitude, behaviour and the way in which we express ourselves. Character, on the other hand, is something we can develop by consciously influencing the way in which we interact with people, and how we respond to life's events. Having identified your colour personality, strengths and weaknesses, you may wish to work on them to build and strengthen your character.

Chapter 9

COLOUR YOUR WORLD

The colours in which you choose to decorate your home are just as important as the colours you wear. In a way, they have a more profound influence on you than the colours of your clothes. Your eyes are not constantly taking in the colours of your clothes, whereas your home decoration surrounds you. And while you can change the colours you wear daily, the colours in your home are relatively permanent. You have to live with them, so before you rush out to buy paint or wallcoverings in your favourite colours from your wheels, remember there is a great deal for you to consider in order to ensure you get the desired results.

You will have many factors with which to juggle, from the size of the room and its use to any fixed features or colours which have to be considered. Furthermore, colour that is lived in defines space, indicates function, suggests temperature and projects personality. If it is your home, you will want at least one room to reflect your innate self. A very powerful force, colour can be used in decorating as it is in clothing – to shrink or stretch entire rooms, and make the not-so-good features disappear.

How Light Affects Room Function

The orientation of different rooms in your home will dictate the time and manner in which light visits them. This will help you decide their best function. Start to become aware that any east-facing rooms will receive early-morning sun. These rooms would therefore make excellent bedrooms or a breakfast room. Rooms facing south are great for living rooms or a kitchen as they will be sunny for most of the day. Rooms with windows or patio doors opening towards the west will catch the sun during the evening and make them wonderful rooms in which to relax and make peace with the world. It is also important to bear in mind that, whichever way the room is facing, the light entering it will not stay constant throughout the day, making it impossible to keep your indoor environment a constant colour.

You may want to balance the natural coolness of a north-facing room by using colours with a warmish undertone. If, however, you enjoy and feel comfortable with the natural cool calmness of this room, you may wish to emphasize it. You can do this by choosing colours from the wheel that fall between green and blue–green, between blue and blue–violet, as well as white and neutral grey. The light in such rooms is ideal for applying make-up or working with colour as it has a minimum of red, orange and yellow wavelengths, and colour changes through the day are minimal.

Using your new-found colour awareness, you can appreciate colour's endless mutability. Understanding the importance of light and the colours it creates will enable you to use it successfully, bringing delight to yourself and others around you. All you have learnt so far in line design and mood will prove invaluable.

The Many Moods of Natural Light

Natural light is constantly changing – from dawn to dusk, season to season, north to south and east to west – affecting the coloured appearance of everything it illuminates. We all experience an emotional response to these colour changes, even though they can scarcely be perceived.

Observe a white or light-neutral room at different times during the day and notice the subtle colour changes. Morning light is a palish yellow or a flat, muted white on a cloudy day. By midday the room will receive white light and look more like the colour it was painted than at any other time. The late afternoon sun has a special character of rich gold which increases in the evening when the sunset produces warm reds. By midnight the light has changed to the deepest blue. Before dawn it takes on a greenish hue, returning to the pale yellow of the dawn. These changes are important when considering interior decorating.

Artificial Light

One of the most underused decorative elements of colour is artificial light. It can exert tremendous influence over the way your room looks and feels in terms of warmth, cheerfulness, drama, excitement and dreariness.

Light plays tricks with the decorative colours you choose. It is essential that you recognize and use the effects that both natural and artificial light create on these colours. Consider what type of light the artificial lighting in your home projects and therefore what affect it will have on the wallcovering or paint colour you are contemplating. When buying decorating materials, bear in mind that the lighting in the store can be misleading. Colours that seem perfect in the store can turn out not to match at all when you bring them home, leading to hours of frustration. Stores tend to favour fluorescent lighting, which is generally cool looking but varies from store to store. This is generally different from the incandescent, warmer lighting found in most homes. Be aware that lampshades focus light differently. Translucent shades provide general illumination whereas opaque shades focus light up towards the ceiling or down on the table top or floor.

Before You Decorate

I gained most of my colour awareness while working in our family decorating business. My main job specification was meeting clients and planning how to redecorate their homes. Before I even thought about a selection of wallcoverings or paints, I used to check which way the room was facing, what function the room was required to have and who was going to use the room. I asked the clients the following questions:

1) **Do you live alone? If not, what do you or other members of your family who will use this room regularly do for a living?**
2) **Do you or any member of your family ever bring work home?**
3) **Does this room have to be multi-purposed (i.e. dining table doubling up for a desk)?**
4) **Do you or other family members get moody or bored?**
5) **Is stress or burn-out a problem from which either you or any member of your family have suffered?**
6) **Do you have any other room in the house where you or other family members congregate to relax and recharge your batteries?**
7) **Do you or your family have any preference for colour?**
8) **Have you or your family given any consideration to style or mood?**
9) **Does any fixed object or furnishing item have to be considered?**
10) **Do you or your family prefer wallcovering or paint? What is your preference for carpet and furniture in this room?**

Other Considerations

There are other questions that you should ask yourself before you begin:
During which part of the day does the room receive natural light? Does the natural light complement the room's function? If not, what will I have to do to counteract its natural inclination?

- **How large or small is the room?**
- **Is the ceiling high or low?**
- **Does the room have any special features which need to be emphasized?**
- **Does the preferred mood or style fit in with everything else, or do we have to compromise?**

If you work in a high-pressure environment which can create overstimulation or stress, then it is vitally important to have a room in your home in which you can relax. This means an environment or atmosphere with an absence of stimulating (advancing) colours. Alternatively, you or a member of your family might have to work in dull, boring or uninspiring environments, in which case you need a room which is uplifting and alive. The advancing colours can do this.

The function of the room and the style and mood which best conveys this are important considerations. As with dress, different looks can be created such as traditional, elegant, glamorous and feminine. Use fabrics, textures, styles, furniture, accessories and lighting to create the right looks for your home.

Choosing Colour

The governing decorative items are paint, wallpaper, curtains, carpets and upholstery. Colour accents come from rugs, lampshades and linens. An area dominated by neutrals can look a bit boring or lifeless. Adding colour accents with accessories, or by repainting some of the area, will bring life to it.

There are more than 2,000 paint colours from which to choose. Paint manufacturers supply cards with sample 'paint chips' on them. Although very useful when planning a colour scheme, they will never give a proper sense of what a painted room will look like. An illustration of a whole room that has been decorated in a particular colour will give you a better overall impression. Photographs of finished rooms can usually be found in paint manufacturer' brochures, as well as in home-decorating magazines and books.

In a larger area, most colours will look darker, stronger or brighter. You can raise or lower a ceiling and square-off long, narrow spaces with the use of advancing and receding colours. In effect, you can create the illusion of distance, space or closeness at will.

Small rooms look more spacious when decorated in a single, light colour such as white or white with a hint of colour. Bright colours foreshorten, and must be used judicially because of their impact. They can be cheering in hallways, stairs and lobbies which are seen mainly in passing, or in rooms which are not in constant use. Large areas of strong or dark colours make an accessorizing amount of white or a light colour appear brighter as, for example, on a cornice or moulding.

Primary colours stimulate, but unbroken areas of bright greens, blues, reds and yellows tend to be overwhelming or even depressing, especially if two or three of these colours meet without a break. Stopping the eye with a sharp contrast in colour can subconsciously set limits on space. The secret of using primary colours for stimulus without letting them overpower a room is to break them up with neutral colours such as white, beige or grey. Strong primary colours work best in sunny south-facing rooms. In dark rooms they have a tendency to look sombre. Yellow in particular needs strong light to look right unless you are using white with a hint of yellow.

You will appreciate by now that colour can be unpredictable. Not all cool colours recede and not all warm colours advance, as their intensity and clarity, and not just their undertone, also play their part. To help you judge a colour, trace some of the room settings or sketch your own room and colour the walls, adding accessory colours to give you some idea of what it will look like. If it works on your picture, it will work in your room.

Adapting Existing Rooms

You do not have to decorate rooms from scratch in order to change them significantly. A room can, for example, look 'busy' if it has been decorated in too many colours or if one colour has been overdone. This effect can be alieviated by taking away some of the colour or minimizing the amount of advancing colour.

Alternatively, a room may look colourless and lack character. A colour can be like a friend which greets you as you open the door, so make the room more friendly by adding colour. Start to become aware of the light which reaches the room, then look at your colour wheel and try imagining where you think a little colour would improve its look. Maybe you have a scarf, picture, scatter cushions or a rug in another room which resembles the colour you would like to add. You will need at least two or three splashes of the same colour to make it work. Vary the amounts of colour between the pieces and distance them correctly, making sure you do not place them all on the same side of the room. Use the colour you have chosen in a major way in one area, repeating it in a smaller amount in another, with other touches somewhere else for emphasis. Keep all colours in place for a while as it sometimes takes time to come to terms with the colour you are experimenting with.

Ring the Changes Seasonally

You can ring the changes seasonally by switching around curtains, cushions, rugs, sidelamps and their bulbs. Use the lightest and brightest colours from your colour wheels for spring, softening the tone for summer, bringing in the warmer tones of your wheels for autumn and finally introducing the stronger and complementary colours for winter. Remember, winter light is greyer, bluer and cooler. Summer light tends to be yellower and warmer.

INDEX